CW00689011

For Ken and Betty
Christmas 2003
Charles

GREEN ODYSSEY

By the same author:
An Age of Saints

GREEN ODYSSEY

Conversion of a geologist

by

Chalwyn James

with foreword and epilogue by Nigel Baird

Change was his mistress; chance his counsellor.
Love held him not; duty forged no chain.
The wide seas and the mountains called him,
And grey dawns saw his camp-fire in the rain.

Anon.

Front cover design by Bryan Barton

Printed and published by
Llanerch Enterprises,
Felinfach, Lampeter,
Ceredigion SA48 8PJ.

ISBN 1-86143-116-3

Reprinted with minor revisions 2003 by
Llanerch Press,
Cribyn, Lampeter,
Ceredigion SA48 7QH.

CONTENTS

INTRODUCTION

Foreword

Although in some ways painful to me, I feel the time has come when I must say something about my relationship with Chalwyn, an odd character whom I seem to have known, off and on, for much of my life.

I hardly know where to begin, but I could perhaps start at Loch Shiel in western Scotland, one misty morning in October over thirty years ago. October in the western Highlands is the time when the mixed birch and pine forest is at its most lovely and the bracken on the lower hills turns a vivid orange, all very appealing on an occasional calm day beneath pale blue skies. But it is also the time when heavy rains begin, the burns fill, the days shorten, and wet storms begin to leave snow on the highest ground. Time therefore for a geologist such as myself to regretfully pack up and leave fieldwork for another year. Now, of course, there is the new road through Moidart. But at that time the only convenient way out of my field area was on the little mail boat that sailed the fresh water of Loch Shiel three times a week.

So, after a quick shave in the bothie where I had been living, I had donned my better clothes and walked down that morning to the tiny pier at Gaskan in good time for the boat. I have always maintained that, although one might be doing fieldwork, one can always look neat and tidy. As often happened, I heard the boat before I could see it. As it loomed out of the mist, I saw that as usual for that time of year there were very few people aboard – on this occasion, just the two crew members and one lone figure standing motionless near the bow, leaning on to a staff. I knew the "skipper" and the "engineer", Donald and Donie, quite well, as I had been doing fieldwork in the area for some years. After the usual friendly banter, I was aboard and we were off. I then turned to look at the other person, the sole passenger, standing alone and silent. "Hello, Nigel," he said and looked me in the eye. For a long moment I stared back. Who was this person who knew my name?

Well, I could see that he was a man of about my own age, slightly stooped, prematurely balding, pale and long of face, bearded, eyes wrinkled, dressed rather scruffily with, of all things, an incongruous pair of sandals on his feet. Although he was looking at me, he seemed to be looking all round me, and through me, and afar, all at the same time. All this I noticed at once, but who was he? "It's been a long time," he added.

Recognition suddenly came. It was Chalwyn, an old friend, or perhaps better said, a colleague from my student days when we had studied geology together and from a later time in Africa when we had worked for rival exploration companies in Zambia, or Northern Rhodesia as it was then known.

After my initial surprise, we chatted and reminisced for forty minutes or so as the tiny mailboat sailed on up the loch. Chalwyn had been living on Iona, but had little interesting to say about the geology. Instead, he spoke of having spent time in the company of some obscure Irish poet there. Eventually the diminutive *Loch Shiel* tied up at Glenfinnan and we continued talking as we walked up the hill to the station. On the way, I showed Chalwyn a large outcrop of fresh metamorphic rocks exposed where blasting had recently widened a corner on the Road to the Isles. I was rather proud of it because, partly at my instigation, this outcrop has been used as a model for designing the entrance to the new part of the Geological Museum in South Kensington. As I explained some of the interesting structures of the rock to Chalwyn – after all, it was in my field area – I noticed again for a moment that far look in his eyes. Was it disinterest, amusement, condescension?

Anyway, we soon reached the railway station, one of the few passing places on the single-track line that parallels the road. The two little trains were duly waiting, facing in opposite directions. We entered our respective trains, found compartments opposite each other, opened the windows, and continued chatting until, with a lot of fussy puffing, the trains pulled out. Mine would take me to Fort William and back south to university. Chalwyn's was to take him west to Mallaig, where he said he would spend a little time walking the nearby hills of Morar before taking passage to the Small Isles, Barra, and other of the Outer Isles.

I sat back in my compartment, quite disconcerted. It had been a brief and inconclusive encounter. There had been a curious symmetry about it, almost as if predestined. Looked at as a statistical probability, it was amazing that it had ever happened at all. There were also lots of unanswered questions, notably Chalwyn's changed appearance and manner.

Well, in a busy life as geologist and college lecturer, there are a great many things to occupy one, and the strange meeting slowly faded from my conscious thoughts. A couple of years later, however, I ran into Chalwyn again in Oxford, where I continued to meet him many times thereafter. His appearance did not change much – a sort of middle-aged hippie. His life style was bizarre and seemed to consist of travelling aimlessly to remote places in Wales, Ireland, Brittany, and the Hebrides, with occasional forays farther afield to Iceland, Newfoundland, Scandinavia, Galicia, the eastern Mediterranean, India, Nepal, and Hokkaido. Between these visits he lived either somewhere with his family in the Welsh border or in Oxford where he retained a wretched room in Ship Street. On a couple of occasions he took me there – a kind of small semicircular den built high up in the thick walls of a turret in a section of the old city wall that I never knew existed, as it is discreetly hidden behind the houses and shops of the Broad.

While in Oxford, Chalwyn seemed to haunt the history sections of the libraries of his own college, Brasenose, and the Radcliffe Camera that face each other just a few yards apart across the cobbled square. He seemed to be interested in such things as Dark Age history, biographies of saints (which I find grossly exaggerated and unbelievable), and things Irish, Welsh and Breton, eastern religions and mythology in general. He sometimes appeared on High Table at Brasenose, where he seemed to get on well with one or two of the dons. I once invited him to high table in my college, Oriel, but I never repeated the invitation – he seemed embarrassingly out of place, withdrawn, and created a very bad impression.

He was more communicative with me, but only at times. For some reason I seemed to amuse him. Even then, at best, what came out from him were incomplete and, I strongly suspect, doctored reminiscences. Some of them were odd, not to say subversive, but I found them in some way moving. So much so that I began to make a note of some of them at the time. In addition to these few notes of mine, Chalwyn bequeathed me material that he himself had written. A picture has emerged, almost like a montage of dreams. I think I have come to understand it and I think it worth the telling.

So, again, where logically to begin? I now have enough information to piece together, from one source or another, a continuous biographical narrative of Chalwyn, even from his childhood days. Nevertheless, on reflection it seems to me that I can only present his story in a sequence indicated by his own scribbled notes. I have already mentioned our extraordinary chance meeting in Loch Shiel – that would have been in the autumn of 1965. Now, in order to supply some essential information, I have to go back to the autumn of 1949, when we first met.

First, however, a few brief words about myself. After prep school near my home in Surrey, I went to boarding school at Chandlebury. It was all rather ordinary and uneventful. I enjoyed most sports, especially rowing, and tolerated classes. Having no particular abilities in science or languages, I took English and Geography in the sixth form. I anticipated leaving school and finding a place with my uncle in the City, working at the head offices of Rhodesian Selection Trust, a large mining corporation with interests mainly in southern Africa. In the meantime, however, my school had put me in for Oxford. Somewhat to my surprise, after submitting what I thought had been some unflattering entrance exam papers, I was called to an interview, a don-rag we used to call it, at Oriel College, where my school enjoyed some tied places. I thought the dons were a drowsy and disinterested bunch. One asked me which side I rowed, and there was a flicker of interest when I told them I could row both sides; in fact I was bow in my school's first eight and I stroked the second four.

Thus it was that, after being conscripted and obtaining a short-term commission in the 8th Hussars tank regiment, a fairly gentlemanly outfit, I went up to Oxford in October 1949. I decided to read geology for the practical experience it might provide. I also thought that it would not make great intellectual demands. To my surprise, I found that I actually enjoyed it, and eventually obtained a respectable second-class degree. Without ever being brilliant at geology, I think I can claim to have made a successful career at it. I attribute this success to a reasonable capacity for discipline and work, steady progress through the ranks of Freemasonry, and a disinclination to get side-tracked in silly things like the arts, politics, student affairs, and endless chit-chat over coffee, such as many students tended to fritter away their time in doing.

It was well into that Michaelmas Term of 1949 when I first met Chalwyn, who had also come up to Oxford that year. I must say that he struck me as being a very young and immature freshman, his behaviour alternating between brash and embarrassingly sensitive, certainly not well-bred. Politically, he was naively socialist. He had not done military service, which I think would have inculcated some character and discipline into him. His accent had perceptible overtones of Welsh and somewhere more northern. One wondered, in fact, if Oxford had spread its net a little wide in admitting him. Although he never mentioned it at the time, and never wore the scholar's gown he should have done, he had in fact won a prestigious entrance scholarship. I learnt afterwards that he had scandalised his college, who expected him under the terms of the scholarship to attend college evensong three times a week, by telling them that he was an atheist and could not therefore honourably do so. Almost in the same breath he had had the cheek to ask his college chaplain if he could use the chapel piano for practice. In spite of all this, he got on well with the chaplain who apparently liked and supported him. His scholarship had been in mathematics, and he had also upset his college greatly by deciding half-way through his first term to switch to geology, which some of his dons regarded as unscholarly, even sacrilegious. One of them, having once read Lyell, had suggested, in a friendly spirit of compromise, that God had indeed created the world according to Genesis but at the commencement of the Cambrian Period, only to be brusquely contradicted by Chalwyn.

Already during his time as a student Chalwyn showed signs of weirdness, although he was also capable of decisive action. As an illustration of this, one small incident particularly sticks in my mind. We were on a field trip in Cumbria led by our professor and happened to be near Shap granite quarry. I remember Chalwyn musing and staring at the lorries struggling over the steep summit on the old A6 (this was in the days long before the present M6), and saying to us something to the effect that we too should look and pay respect for here was the country's artery throbbing. It was the kind of remark, rather typical of him, which no one knew whether to take seriously or not. Then suddenly there was a boom when the quarry blasted and to our horror we saw some rock fragments rising and then falling in our direction, although we had been advised that we were working in a safe position. Chalwyn dived for Prof, felled him as in a rugby tackle, and lay across his head while protecting himself by cupping his hands behind his own head. No one was in fact hit, and Prof picked himself up, growled something like "no need to overdramatize matters, Chalwyn", and the field trip continued. Nevertheless, I think Prof was impressed. The following year he included Chalwyn on an important expedition to East Greenland. There too Chalwyn acted the dreamer and sometimes puzzled or annoyed other expedition members, but apparently redeemed himself by an act of seamanship in a small boat on a critical occasion. When he got back Chalwyn told us they had not gone with love to the Arctic but with the intention of raping it!

In our student days, the government would pay two Pounds and five shillings per week support for student's field work, and Chalwyn would find excuses to obtain this money and use it to travel alone in places like Western Ireland and the Hebrides. I was not convinced that his time was all honestly spent on geological fieldwork on these trips. I remember also that most of us were assigned field areas for our finals mapping project. Characteristically, Chalwyn chose his own, a remote peninsula in the Isle of Mull on the medieval pilgrim route to Iona. Later, he did his graduate research on an inaccessible and mountainous area of the nearby Isle of Rum, where I once joined him for a week in his camp, situated in a lonely valley and provisioned by sea.

Chalwyn was fascinated by "continental drift" and twice while a student presented material on this subject in seminars, after having read very unfashionable authors and collected ill-sorted data. I recall that he was shot down on both occasions. The subject of continental drift was taboo and considered impossible and unscientific by responsible geologists. I recall Chalwyn saying: "It must be true; it explains so much by so little." Ironically, only years later did the mechanism of what we all now accept as "plate tectonics" become apparent. I remember Chalwyn later saying to me that the mechanism of a revolution in thought, people's reactions to new paradigms, and the phenomenon of personal conversion were all vital lessons that geologists should teach, so that people might once again return to the proper worship of Gaia. Weird!

There were times, however, when Chalwyn acted quite normally. Rather untypically for such an obvious loner, for a time he enjoyed the team sport of rowing and rowed bow in his college eight, although he later forsook this for solitary sculling on the Isis and Cherwell in the early mornings. The one activity that brought us together socially a few times was dinghy sailing on the river at Port Meadow, where we quite happily took turn and turn about as helmsman and crew on an erratic course up-river to the *Trout* – and an even more erratic one back!

But Chalwyn remained essentially a loner. When I met up with him again later as a field geologist in central Africa, it was well recognised that he much preferred to work by himself on small properties of tin, beryl, and chromite, rather than in a team on large-scale copper prospects. He lasted far longer than anyone else in Charter Exploration's notoriously difficult Zambezi Concession, where he went a bit native and came to be known as "Zambezi Charlie". On leaving Africa, his geological career was seriously compromised when he went off on several years vagabonding around the Mediterranean followed by a year schoolteaching. There was also a failed marriage, which I imagine must have been very painful for him as he seldom spoke of it. Later, he did a long spell of university teaching in Canada. He wrote a book on geology. It was panned by some critics, but liked by students. He completed another with the provisional title "Mother Earth and the Future of Humanity", which was never published. He once showed me the ms, a strange mixture of science and ethics. He told me with a chuckle that when he prematurely resigned from his Canadian university post, he gave a final lecture on the theme of "Gaia and the Pysche" to his class of geology students. Typical!

Now I come to the most surprising thing of all. It pains me, but it has to be mentioned. Just after Chalwyn's death, I learnt by chance that we were in fact closely related! I do not know for certain if Chalwyn was aware of this. I suspect now that he was, although he never hinted of it to me at any time. Apparently, his mother's side of the family came from an out-of-wedlock liaison which had been kept a close secret from both the families of our generation. The liaison was a long-standing one between my grandfather, whom one could describe as an eccentric but successful Liverpool merchant, and a beautiful servant-girl of Irish descent. We were thus half-cousins! There was in fact a similarity in features and build between us, and our ages also happened to be close. Once, I remember at a party in Northern Rhodesia someone christened us the terrible twins (I didn't appreciate this), but I had always ascribed any resemblance to coincidence, and had never given the matter another thought.

When I learnt the truth, I used to think that had he received a better upbringing (his family remained poor) Chalwyn might have been more normal, perhaps more like myself. I also reflected that, had our circumstances been reversed, I might have ended up like Chalwyn – a sobering thought which I quickly dismissed as impossible. But sometimes, when I think about him, as I now seem to do more and more frequently, it seems to me that what happened in our lives and careers was an ongoing divergence in development, one of us developing the practical, the other the spiritual. Perhaps the two should come together! Indeed, I seem to have reached a point in my late years where I cannot now declare with conviction which one of us was "right".

For example, speaking myself as a "practical" hard-headed geologist, I have come to realise that Chalwyn, "the dreamer", was right about such matters as our abuse of Earth's natural resources, an inevitable coming Dark Age, and the need for "ethical" responses to what may appear at first sight to be "practical" problems facing mankind.

So I feel rather strongly therefore that I must now let Chalwyn speak, albeit posthumously, for himself.

Chalwyn died in fact just a few months after he had confided to me in a matter-of-fact manner that he had dreamt of his coming death. What he left to me were a collection of short stories, some incomplete, some in note form, diary material, some quotations that had obviously appealed to him, and even a few lines of verse. I have tried to tidy things up and I have presented material in the order in which Chalwyn himself had tentatively put it – "in chronological order of psyche-revelation", as Chalwyn once said to me in his typically maddening manner! I still disapprove of the personal and political nature of some of the material (and especially my appearance in Chalwyn's dreams!), but I have included most of it nonetheless. Some of the material I know to be factual, whereas in some the facts have undoubtedly been embroidered. I apologise for any awkwardness of style or repetition caused by the nature of the material and my handling of it.

So here is Chalwyn's story, beginning with *Kweku*, apparently first drafted on his return from Africa.

Nigel Baird
Oxford, 2001

* * * * * * *

Kweku

I am back in the homeland of my fathers: this hilly border country of hedged green fields and copses, with the sheep grazing scattered and peaceful, the dairy herds in the valley leas, and here and there a south-facing slope under the plough. Every other field has a pheasant or two, and not far away a pair of buzzards are circling and mewing. As Alan Paton once said of the African hills of Lesotho is his *Cry The Beloved Country*, these Welsh Border hills are "lovely beyond the singing of them". Behind me are the brown and purple moors, cut in one place by a long ribbon of short green turf rising westward to the distant pass, a former drovers' trail. And beyond the moors there are glimpses of high blue rocky mountains far away in the west. My distant ancestors used to drive sheep, ponies, and Welsh Black cattle over this trail from the far valleys of Gwynedd, Lleyn, and Anglesey to sell in the border market town and far beyond. Strange that whenever I think of my ancestors, it is of my father's side, and not of my mother's. Indeed, I know remarkably little about the latter, although their spirits must be just as real and speak just as often to my psyche.

The border town lies in view below me now, always busy, and busy beyond belief on market day, Wednesday. It grew around the castle or, more precisely, between the two fortresses, one of earth and one of stone, that between them span two thousand years of border history, situated where our hills meet the English plain. Much further away, on a clear fresh day like today with a cleansing west wind, one can distinguish the English city and the high square tower of its cathedral, built on a shallow hill between the shining curves of Britain's largest river. This whole panorama from the hill known as the Moelydd is one of my earliest childhood memories. As our fresh mountain streams feed the big river, so for generations some of us have sought our fortune in the English plain or even further away. How little did I ever dream that my own Odyssey was to take me so far – only to finally realise that the answer to my quest lay within!

But this place where I often return is my border homeland, my "patria chica" as the Spaniards say. When a young child, it was my preferred place for idyllic summer holidays. Not long after, it became a safe refuge when my Merseyside home was bombed in the war. In those days, the 70-acre farm, Ty Newydd, was worked with three horses in a style very probably not all that different from when the "new" farmhouse itself had been built four centuries ago. I have never ceased to revisit this place.

Reminders of border history are never far away and invite one to journey back in time. The green mound of Owain Glyndwr's castle lies just over the hill. The nearby Llanymynech Hill witnessed the last stand of Caradoc against the Romans. Its name, "settlement of the monks", refers to Celtic saints who first lived there over twelve centuries ago. And this low green stony ridge on which I am sitting now, running each side of our stackyard and indeed for miles over the hills to the north and to the south, was in fact the ancient border which at one time had peacefully and sensibly separated Saxon from Celt.

Solitary walkers of the new long-distance path now follow the nearby green lane, overhung by ash trees and edged by violets, primroses, and arum lilies in Spring, and a profusion of dog-roses, cinquefoil, rock-rose, wild mignonette, agrimony, lady's bedstraw, water avens, bellflowers, hardheads and meadowsweet in midsummer, to be followed in turn by flowers of basil and wild marjoram and a crop of damsons and hazel nuts. They pass the "rough", a small overgrown limestone quarry, where my cousin planted a rowan grove not long before he died.

Last night I had looked again at the old family bible. There men long dead had recorded their children, themselves dead too, the birthplaces reading like a gazetteer of this part of the border: Meifod, Llanymynech, Pen-y-bont, Trefonen, Llanfyllin, and many more. Put any of us anywhere in this part of the border country and we instinctively feel at home and we are known. It was five generations since we forsook droving for farming and we are now part of this country, and this country is part of us. Nowhere along the whole Welsh Border is the demarcation between hill and plain, between Welsh and English speaking, so marked as it is here. I know some people may consider us border folk devious, two-faced even. It is true that we *do* look both ways – to the east for trade and often a livelihood, but to the west for our spiritual life. But we do not lack integrity.

A skylark stops singing as it plummets to earth quite close to me with a final chirrup. Suddenly there seems to be silence, broken only by the softly sighing breeze. Then, as my ears adjust to the relative quiet, I can hear the faint call of a cuckoo in a nearby wooded valley. A late-Spring commonplace, but its intermittent call seems to say Kweku, Kweku, Kweku, my last African name, Kweku, Kweku, born on Thursday, Kweku, Kweku, the cunning one, Kweku, how did they know I was born on a Thursday, Kweku they called me and smiled. I close my eyes and clutch the green turf, but even the homely cuckoo does not allow me to forget my Africa – and so much more. For it was indeed Africa that provided the key that was to unlock so much that was within.

So, the memories flood back, unbidden. I am old enough to know, now, that the most important thing of all is to live one's life so that one's memories are good ones that are comfortable to die with. Can one ever atone for the bad memories?

> Before setting forth on that inevitable journey, none is wiser than the man who considers – before his soul departs hence – what good or evil he has done, and what judgement his soul will receive after its passing.
>
> Cuthbert

It has been my lot to have been a traveller on all of the oceans and continents of this lovely blue planet – Herself a lone wanderer in a space-time continuum of mind-numbing dimensions. Travel implies time, but our human lifespans are so short that in truth they represent merely a "still" in the evolving "cine" picture of the aeons of geological time. More importantly, I see also now, at last, that my wandering – travel seems almost too purposive a word – was an education in psychic awareness that transcends time.

On the way, did I personally waste too much time on a conventional career, annoying my professional colleagues the while by pretending to be a geologist? Or did perhaps the experience of geology, eventually and after all, help in various ways to lead to some important realisations?

> If a man must play the hypocrite to find his path to destiny, then so be it.
>
> from *Scarlet and Black* by Stendhal

Simply told, it seems that I was trained to rape Earth, but I fell in love with Her instead.

> He putteth forth his hand upon the rock; he overturneth the mountain by the roots.
> He cutteth out rivers among the rocks; and his eye sees every precious thing.
> He bindeth the floods from overflowing; and the thing that is hid he bringeth to light.

> But where shall wisdom be found? And where is the place of understanding?
>
> Job, 28: 9-12

These little stories and reflections – like stills frozen by my memory's projector from my own tiny finite cine of a life – can perhaps therefore reveal a story of a search for identity and meaning. Is it an example of a path to one's roots that each one of us may eventually follow? Or do some die without ever becoming aware of the path's existence? It is very clear to me now that my search, although apparently unwitting, was in fact driven relentlessly by my psyche. This compilation then is not primarily about "me". The "i" is not important. Rather, the i was merely the agent for the much deeper forces that are present in each of us, if only we give them rein and admit them to our consciousness.

Chalwyn James
Ty Newydd

> You may say i'm a dreamer,
> But i'm not the only one.
>
> John Lennon, *Imagine*

> . . . for even quite common men have souls.
>
> R. H. Tawney in *Religion and the Rise of Capitalism*

PART I AFRICAN AWAKENING

Flight to Africa

"Travel by day, sleep by night, much safer, more restful, see more, cheaper too." With the seductive phrases of the travel agent still ringing in my ears, I paused on the apron at Heathrow and took a hard look at reality in the form of a small two-engined unpressurised Viking impertinently parked among the aristocratic Constellations and DC6's. Would it get me to Johannesburg, even with a generous time allowance of five days compared with the larger planes' thirty hours? However, I was committed now along with an ill-assorted group of old-timers and fellow emigrants. Flying is a bore now, but it was just a little bit of an adventure then, especially one's first flight.

Joining the queue of taxi-ing planes, our turn eventually came in a deafening shaking racket at full throttle enlivened by exhaust smoke and sparks. We soon left England with its distressing patterns of suburbs eating like cancers into a wounded countryside, and crossed the narrow sea "as a moat defensive to a wall" crowded with ships great and small which left their wakes as the only evidence of motions that were otherwise imperceptible to us. Then French fields and a distant view of Paris – what a reserve of agricultural land and peasantry there is in this most civilised country. At Nice our young Rhodesian pilot, who liked to be called captain, said we were to go "ashore" for an hour. We happened to sit together over lunch where perhaps he thought I looked as if I needed reassuring: "Look man, we don't have to fly over the Alps like those big bastards, we fly through them."

Off again over a warmer, bluer, and kinder sea cradling hilly islands, white cities and legends, and on towards our overnight stop in Malta. I enjoyed an evening stroll through busy streets among people who were pleasant and relaxed, living for the present, and seemingly determined to forget their confused and recurring history of invaders, settlers, pirates, crusaders, and others. Will there be historians a millennium from now, I wondered, to record the achievements of us wonderful westerners, who abandon all former Gods for the money-god, who rape our good Earth, and squabble with each other like greedy vultures while we do so? How we made poor Malta suffer in freedom's name the last time round – she has had so many crosses to bear.

Next day, after another long hop over the sea, we enjoyed coffee in the desert near the north African coast, a new and unfamiliar flag hanging limply in the hazy heat over airport buildings originally built for war. With full tanks and after a staggering crawling take-off we began a very long monotonous flight over the desert with glimpses of curving cuestas of sculptured sand and occasional red and yellow ridges and scarps of rock. Otherwise it was a matter of boredom, heat, soft drinks, bumps, and air sickness. On and on and on with the starboard blinds fully drawn against the blinding sun, everyone exhausted, and the first taste of dust, the dust of Africa that I was to come to know so well.

Early evening witnessed the miracle of the Nile. I quietly watched fishermen at work and also the busy pied kingfishers fluttering and diving under the river-hugging palms. Beyond these lay nothing but desert. Sleep was impossible in the moored river-boat at Wadi Halfa that the airline used as a hotel as fans blew hot air at 100° through the night. Two days and we have barely reached black Africa!

The next morning we had an early start but we were just beaten to the plane by the sun, rising enormous and red. Within a very few minutes it was silvery yellow and burning hot. Up river, we had an extended stay in Khartoum: "Hydraulics again, always having trouble with them, probably the dust." First an hour's delay, then another two hours, during which time a south-bound Constellation, that most graceful of aeroplanes, derisively landed and took off again on schedule after forty-five minutes of frenzied activity by ground staff. So in the end we stayed the night.

As consolation, however, we enjoyed a late-afternoon impromptu tour round Khartoum in two mini-buses with a voluble Egyptian guide and erratic Sudanese drivers, courtesy of the airline. I slipped away from my party at a spot overlooking the meeting of the two Niles – the one wide, placid and blue with huge perch lazily jumping below wheeling hawks and gulls, the other muddy and turbulent with small standing waves. Curiously, their waters did not seem to mingle for as far as the eye could see beyond their confluence. Each kept its character even beyond where the distant silver dome of the caliph's palace rose above the old city of Omdurman, where a mad Scot had perished unforgettably in the glorious days of empire. I watched a fairly large clinker-built boat with a crew of six taking on a cargo of bundles of faggots, using as a crane a tapering beam about thirty feet long attached at about a third of its length to the mast. Later I saw the boat in progress: two men in the stern were poling;

the rest were hauling on a long rope attached to the bow. The speed was no more than about one mile per hour against the current, all to the accompaniment of wailing singing. How much of this had changed, I wondered, since biblical times?

I walked back alone to the teeming market in the centre of the new city of Khartoum, along one of the eight converging roads built in the pattern of the Union Jack (what arrogance!), all cluttered with camel caravans, mostly carrying faggots. The market traders were friendly – I bought a silk tie that I didn't need at all at a very reasonable price!

Next morning we left this busy city to fly on southwards over the huge irrigated triangle of cotton plantations between the two Niles. Then, quite suddenly, we were back over desert again. But now we watched the slow change from desert to sudan with scattered thorn bushes and then to sahel country with grass between scattered taller trees. "We're going down to cruise at 600 feet to see if we can see any game," said the captain. It felt like we were skimming the treetops. Silently I wondered if this was in line with airline regulations and remembered the anxious mother's advice to her airman son: "Fly low and slow, dear." However, there was nothing for it but to relax and enjoy the sight of great herds of buck, numerous elephant, a small family of surprised rhino at a waterhole, and several herds of giraffe loping away with a deceptively easy gait. "Well, you wouldn't see that from a Constellation," said our gallant captain. The Constellation we had seen yesterday was certainly in Johannesburg by now.

We refuelled at Juba, a fetid dump on the upper Nile. The take-off was chiefly remarkable for a thunderstorm cum cloudburst just beyond the end of the runway which we had to make a steep climbing turn to avoid. I think our captain was beginning to enjoy himself. Later that afternoon I visited him in the cockpit, where he was sitting with something resembling a school atlas on his lap open at East Africa. He was crooning to himself while endeavouring to weave around some of the bigger of the white billowing cumulus clouds in our path, not without some severe bumps.

That evening, when the red dust of our landing on the laterite runway of Nairobi had dispersed, we could see two great snow-capped mountains between the dying thunder clouds. Although we were almost exactly on the equator the air at an altitude of 6000 feet was pleasantly cool. Nairobi itself was a surrealist world where the whites routinely carried their revolvers, rifles and bandoliers into the bars of the new luxury hotels that fronted the wide tree-lined dual carriageway, watched by the little brown sharp-eyed Kikuyu, tall black policemen, and turbaned and urbane Indians. A bizarre imperial dream that was ending in tragedy.

Another dawn start and on again over hundreds and hundreds of miles of the flat savannah country of northern Tanganyika, the scene dramatically broken by glimpses of improbably high volcanoes and lakes in deep rift valleys. I remember at one point looking down on a lake with pink skeins of flamingos tracing patterns over floating cakes of salt and then noticing the steep forested slopes of a volcano appearing surprisingly close above us on the other side of the plane.

I suffered a sudden pang of loneliness. Each day meant another 1200 miles of this vast, majestic, but alien continent between me and my homeland. Too many impressions had crowded indigestibly into my mind and I took refuge in slumber.

I woke up drowsily. The everlasting bush was now broken by a narrow orange ribbon – the great north road of Northern Rhodesia. We followed it closely but I couldn't see any vehicles. Our captain let a ten-year-old take the controls in the co-pilot's seat. The plane gently bucked and dipped. The boy returned from the cockpit, eyes shining. He wouldn't forget that moment quickly. We left the line of the road for a more grassy kind of bush, a great grassy plain in fact, with lazy loops and lakes of still water, and dotted here and there with large herds of reddish-brown antelope, tens of thousands of them. Much later that afternoon we arrived exhausted at Salisbury after wearisome stops at Kasama and Lusaka and after crossing yet another great rift valley, the Zambezi, a now evocative name for me on account of adventures that were yet to come.

We spent the last night of the voyage in Salisbury, capital of Southern Rhodesia, 5000 feet up and compared by some to Nairobi, but the countryside certainly lacked the beauty of Kenya, that most lovely of countries. Salisbury seemed to be a white man's city in a white settler country. It was replete with numerous blocks of offices, shops, and apartment buildings set between very wide avenues, designed originally by Cecil Rhodes, so I was told, in order that an eight-span ox team could be turned in them with ease, but now choked with shiny new cars. At dusk I visited the lonely ironstone kopje that overlooks the sprouting city, built out of that one man's dream:

> The immense and brooding spirit still shall quicken and control,
> Living he was the land, and dead his soul shall be her soul.

It was difficult to imagine that evening that the southern Cape of Africa was still 1500 miles away and we were all too exhausted to think about the morrow anyway. Next morning we flew "only" over another eight hundred miles of veldt broken by yet another great river – "the grey green greasy Limpopo". We finally reached Johannesburg whose main street runs along the Witwatersrand, the outcrop of the world's richest gold reef. Johannesburg was surrounded by huge yellow tips of crushed mine waste that rivalled the city buildings in height. "Joli, that white men call Johannesburg, the city of gold" – but that is another story.

I had arrived. In the course of just a few days, it seemed that Britain, where I had spent most of my life, had suddenly become a faint memory. My mind was like a computer disc, recently erased, but formatted with plenty of room to receive new messages.

* * * * * * *

Robbie

After some weeks working in the bushveld I left Joli and flew back north to Northern Rhodesia to join the field staff of a company known as Chartered Exploration. After flying again over the Limpopo and Zambezi rivers I found myself looking intently at the wide zone of steep hilly country on the north side of the Zambezi rift valley. It seemed very much more mysterious, more African, than the country to the south. Moreover, it was the terrain in which I understood I was to work. Just a few small villages of red mud and grass huts lay scattered among the endless greenery. The thought crossed my mind: how did one get around this kind of country? (Answer: by ox-cart or land-rover as far as practicable, and then by foot on native paths, "sendas", or even better, on wider and well-engineered elephant trails!). These thoughts ended as the small plane started to descend towards a single track railway line paralleled by a red dirt road, and made a bumpy landing at Lusaka.

A few days later, I travelled back along that same dirt road for about 150 miles to Monze. My first thoughts of Monze were that it was the end of the civilised world, a Fawcett-like outpost in the jungle. Indeed, it consisted of little more than a railway siding, a garage run incredibly efficiently by a Lancashire man with a native wife, two Indian stores, a few mud huts, and a "hotel" also built of mud. Later on, Monze seemed to me to be the epitome of civilisation!

From there, I turned off to join my first camp, situated not far from Gwembe boma where the District Commissioner had his lonely bungalow. Like a teacher his first class, I remember well my first camp, the first of a very great number, although many of the rest have become a blur in my memory. I remember my tent beneath a flame tree and my wash-stand below a honeysuckle bush near a huge eroded anthill covered in fireball lilies. I remember the bream in the nearby lake with its many duck, spur-wing geese, an occasional jacanda walking over the lily pads, a colony of yellow weaver birds, and a nest of the bizarre hammerhead. I remember the kingfishers, some blue, some black and white, all much bigger and far less shy than those of the Vyrnwy. And, I nearly forgot to mention, I remember also the familiar swallows that had also come all the way from Europe. Later, I was to keep a bird log which recorded well over three hundred different species, many of which I came to know well.

But first there were many items of a practical nature to learn. Now in order to run efficiently, every bush camp has to have a "boss-boy", equivalent, let us say, in nautical terms to a boson. Our boss-boy was Robbie. My first visual impressions of Robbie were two: an apparently permanent cloth cap of a shape worn by north British working men but in a very coarse check pattern, and very prominent front teeth with spaces between them. But Robbie was OK. Indeed, he was one of the best, irascible at times with the men, but reasonable to all.

Robbie was a great singer. I recall on one much later occasion travelling with him late one afternoon on a lorry crawling up the new road, in fact the only road, leading up from the Zambezi rift valley to the plateau. It was in the middle of the long dry season, winter if you like. Although the valley was always nice and warm (this could be an understatement at times!), dry-season nights on the plateau were cool and could even see a touch of ground frost. The men were already cold and shivering and I was apprehensive of the possible effects of fever on those with endemic malaria. But Robbie started to sing our lorry song. Soon all were joining in the repeated chorus:

A little faster, a little faster;
Driver, driver, beat that motor.

(I'm afraid it loses its rhythm in translation). Robbie sang the stanzas, improvising exaggerated adventures about earthly trials and delights such as safaris, animals, meat, women, and the idiosyncrasies of bwanas. The cold was soon lost among the laughter. An enormous full moon rose as the sun set and, shortly after pitching camp, Robbie had seen to it that there was a good fire going. He looked after us all.

Much later, Glen and I took Robbie to the little mission hospital when he had suddenly become very ill. Robbie was very depressed there. I was quite sure that he just wanted to go home. It was typical of him that he stifled such thoughts even when we asked him directly if we could help. Oh, he was sure he would get better here, the doctor had listened to his chest with the cold piece of metal on a string. We asked the doctor about Robbie. Well, his heart was very dicky indeed, it was tired, he would never be really well, he just had to rest for the moment, etc. Glen and I exchanged a glance, as we remembered the long, strenuous, sweating, and sometimes frustrating days of the previous year, and the seemingly untiring Robbie.

Robbie had been promoted to boss-boy on account of his extreme conscientiousness. He earned an extra threepence a day on top of the normal daily wage of eighteenpence. I saw him once with a bottle of "strength" medicine. He confided that he used his extra pay to buy this medicine so that he could work well. He had bought it at the Indian store in Monze, the one with a chart of the human body on a large board with numbers on. The numbers ran from 1 to 22 and indicated various parts of the body. The idea was that if you were sick you looked at the chart, noted the number of where it hurt (eyes, ears, chest, tummy, etc. – I won't go into all the explicit details) and requested the appropriate medicine. The Indian had a cabinet of shelves with 22 compartments, each containing bottles or packets of muti. Simple. The cost of each was seven shillings and six pence. A new English lady doctor, who visited Monze once a fortnight in her railway-coach clinic, was appalled at all this. She offered to diagnose and provide medicine for two shillings and sixpence a consultation, or less if people could not afford to pay. She was not popular – her muti was clearly not as powerful as the Indian's because it cost so little!

Perhaps we westerners underestimate how much sickness begins in the mind. Indeed, we seem to be largely oblivious to this. Perhaps also we put an inflated value on prolonging individual life. We are all mortal. When the time comes to die may it not be better, whether we be young or old, in war or in peace, to die well and in dignity, then to be properly mourned according to custom, than struggle against all-powerful fate? Death is the great equaliser. I read the other day that a British life-insurance company was starting to do good business with middle-class Africans! Bully for them.

Shortly later, on a second visit, when I had gone hoping to pick up Robbie and take him home, I found him very weak indeed. I was actually holding his hand when he quietly passed away. That same week I had found myself assisting the mission nurse at a birth out in the bush near my camp. So I had been a witness of birth and death, both for the first time, within a few days.

Robbie knew he was going to die before we ever took him to the hospital. One dawn in camp during the rainy season I happened to watch him unobserved. After heavy overnight rain, a scotch mist was still gently soaking the greenery. Robbie was up near the open kitchen leaning against one of the rough poles that supported its thatched roof. Pedro, my cook, was squatting over the fire staring vacantly out over the shallow grassy valley to where the mist touched the trees on the other side. The men were slowly wending their way in single file along the new path between the high wet grass up the slope towards us. Robbie was singing to himself. His song was quite different from any of the usual rhythmic dancing or clapping songs of Africa. It was like a sad haunting ballad with an intricate melody. I thought he was singing of the rain and the morning. I had just been reading a biography of Livingstone, which quoted a diary entry of his to the effect of being surprised once by a primitive African describing Heaven to him in terms like this: "When copious rains have descended on the land and the early sun rising reflects in a drop of water on each blade of grass and all is clean and sweet-scented – that is heaven."

I cannot recall the melody of Robbie's song. Indeed, I believe I only heard Robbie sing like that once. Some time afterwards, Pedro told me that on this occasion Robbie had actually been singing of his coming death.

Robbie, my friend, whom I remember, you never wasted time complaining. You played the hand you were dealt with, as well as you possibly could. Who of us can do more?

* * * * * * *

The mission

How quickly the African night follows sundown. It is already quite dark outside. The interior of the large chapel, built of mud walls with a thatched roof, standing inside a circular enclosure of cleared ground hedged by lantana, is warmly lit by hurricane lamps. Their glow is reflected by the several hundred brown faces of the children who are crowded in. They have come for the annual gathering of all the mission's schools in the area, and are waiting to be addressed by the visiting American preacher. The school uniforms of the bigger girls fail to disguise their voluptuous young figures. They and the older boys furtively eye each other, and each group of children whisper among themselves. The youngest boys and girls, crowded on the front benches and floor, turn their heads and gape with wide open eyes at the animated scene over which the murmuring of the chatter rises and falls. There is a momentary hush as the lady teachers come in and take their places at one side in the front. Then the tide of murmuring breaks out again. More children, possibly more than had been anticipated, continue to filter in and quietly find places in the aisles and sides and corners. A white-haired African teacher fusses with the two lamps near the simple lectern.

The preacher is late, but what does that matter? For each of the children just to be there is a kind of living miracle wrought in just over a generation. By their very presence they are bearing witness to the peaceful union of the surrounding villages drawn from an area in which their own fathers had once fought and raided each other. It was completely satisfying and fulfilling just to be there. No more emotion is necessary or even bearable.

The assembly gradually becomes silent as the sound of two handbells can be heard approaching outside. In a great hush all eyes turn to the open door. The two senior boys, with the bells now muted, enter and are followed by the preacher and his local African interpreter who will translate into the vernacular.

Suddenly and irresistibly it comes to me that the scene I am witnessing is what it must have been like in Wales during the "Age of Saints" beginning some fifteen centuries ago. Once numerous mud, wattle, and thatch chapels have completely vanished, leaving behind only a "Llan" name. In a few places ancient yews may persist within a circular churchyard enclosure. Sometimes also a primitive cross inscribed on a rough stone, or more rarely still a bronze Celtic handbell like the one over in the next valley to our Vyrnwy, have survived to provide tangible testimony of a sacred past. But the land remembers.

I am aroused from my reverie when in response to the announcement of what is evidently a favourite hymn number, a note from the African teacher is immediately and confidently followed by a great surge of song in harmony. Jesus, in how many parts of the world is your praise sung like this? The silence after the hymn is a prelude to the lesson read nervously but well by one of the senior boys. After another resounding hymn, the preacher begins, taking for his text the sowing of the seed. Each sentence and gesture is repeated and mirrored by the interpreter, their voices overlapping. Practice and reiteration have apparently not dulled their obvious sincerity and spontaneity. Soon, beads of sweat cover the preacher's face which he wipes hurriedly with a handkerchief and goes on without pausing, repeating himself and together with the interpreter creating a fugue out of a parable.

The message gets across. Rural Galilee and Ila country are one. Abruptly, the preacher pauses. Then come to Jesus, he cries. Before the closing hymn, the interpreter says that those who wish to can remain. During its singing, the children slowly leave, the youngest first, then the older girls followed by the boys. The singing inside is echoed by the voices of the children slowly filing out. The harmony assumes different proportions as the higher pitched voices recede into the sweet African night, but the verses continue to be repeated again and again without cease and with mesmeric effect. Eventually most have gone.

There remain about a dozen of the youths kneeling at the front of the church. Most are crying, one is talking rapidly and cannot be stopped, and one is screaming and throwing himself to the ground with such violence that the teachers attempt to restrain him. The preacher confirms them in the faith attributed to the Jew, Jesus of Nazareth, as interpreted by the Arkansas Seventh Day Apostolic Church.

* * * * * * *

Time

For a long spell I was working by myself, that is to say without a white colleague or assistant. Unlike some geologists working under these conditions I can truthfully say that I never felt lonely in the bush. It was about this time that I stopped wearing a watch. What use was it anyway, if no one else had one? Instead, we knew the time by the position of the sun. One could easily make arrangements by pointing to the appropriate section of the sun's daily path through the sky. For example, a finger pointed horizontally to the east meant a dawn start, one pointed vertically upwards meant a midday meeting, and so on, with refinements. After sunset, I found I could generally estimate time to within ten minutes by observing the lie of the Southern Cross, utilising of course the prominent daily rotation of 15° per hour in the axis of the cross, and taking into account also the more subtle ongoing annual rotation of 30° per month. I enjoyed doing this and seeing how near I could estimate the time of the BBC overseas news broadcast at 9 p.m. If I had been away in town for a few days, it took me two or three evenings to get back to accuracy. Then I stopped listening to the British news anyway. Somehow it seemed to have lost its relevance.

This timelessness extended to days. I tended to work by projects and safaris of a few days duration. If I felt like a rest or a day off shooting I took it. Again, if the men had something on in the village, I might spend the day writing up reports, etc. There was one month when I lost two days and for the life of me couldn't account for them in my monthly report, much to the consternation of head office.

So time passed very contentedly for me. I remember once meeting up in Lusaka with Nigel Baird, a geologist friend from student days, and talking about our lives in the bush. I was amused when he told me of his work in a large team for another exploration company. They had completed a geochemical survey over a large area, and had pinpointed some copper anomalies. They then followed them up in the approved manner, undertook trenching and drilling, and had actually proved a significant copper deposit. Only at this stage apparently did someone decide that the place was too remote from the railway serving the established large mines of the Northern Rhodesian copper belt to be worth developing! For his part, Nigel seemed quite shocked and flabbergasted at my solitary "timeless" existence.

I began to feel the rhythm of the seasons, here dry and wet rather than warm and cool as in temperate latitudes, but not without their subtleties. Over a period of nine years in Black Africa, the longest times I was ever based in one camp were about five months in Tonga country near Masuku and much later on in Southern Rhodesia, when I camped under an unusually tall and trunk-like wisteria tree for six months while pegging and working on some chromite claims. The question of recording the passage of time in years thus never arose.

I became aware of the difficulty of doing this, however, when I once met up with an exceedingly old native man who claimed that when he was a very young child he had seen Livingstone. He had lived all his life in a village near a curious rounded mountain with a shape like an inverted pudding basin. These mountains of bare rock, actually more the size of big hills, are commoner in desert or semi-desert areas of Africa, and this one, Chimwami, is unique in the wooded Zambezi concession area. It is made of granite and is strikingly white in colour. It is rather steep all round the base, but once some initial progress is made up a crack and the coefficient of friction between man and rock has been rather severely tested, the slope eases off and it is possible to walk comfortably to the top. Although it sounds a prominent feature, I am sure very few white men have seen it as it is remote from any road. It is held in considerable veneration by the local people, somewhat as Ayres Rock is by Australian aborigines.

On one of the rare visits paid me by my boss from the local head office in Lusaka, whom I regarded as a hard-bitten man devoid of any sense of humour, he expressed a wish to visit Chimwami, so we went there together.

Chimwami lies in an extension of the "tin-belt" and within the granite of the hill there are indeed just a few white veins of quartz with negligible cassiterite (the ore of tin) in them. My boss got excited and started talking of possibly mining the whole hill as a low-grade deposit, a rival to the Bolivian Potosi! What values had I found? At this moment I recall that we looked at each other in mutual incomprehension and disbelief. The idea of putting a hammer to the hill had never occurred to me as it would have been a sacrilege. In any event, it was possible to see what was there well enough anyway. Conversely, the idea of my not thoroughly investigating the largest outcrop of rock in the whole area was incomprehensible to my poor boss! I burst out laughing. The incident confirmed our worst fears about each other.

However, to get back to my meeting with the old man. Livingstone, in his journals, did indeed record passing within sight of this white mountain after discovering the Victoria Falls. Furthermore, he was almost certainly the only white man to have been in the area until at least some forty years later on. I was interested in checking whether the old man had actually seen Livingstone himself, or whether he had merely been told about Livingstone as a child and had come to believe that he had seen him. I actually had the year of Livingstone's journey, but I discovered that the old man couldn't reciprocate precisely because he did not know his own age! He could remember individual years such as the year of the man-eating lion, the year the elephant trampled his "garden" (a small field of crops), and so on – understandably so! But any exact arithmetical count had been lost over the many years of his long life. Although obviously very old indeed, he was reasonably lucid and coherent. He was vehement that he had personally seen Livingstone. The villagers, moreover, readily confirmed that he really was quite exceptionally old. So I believed him and accordingly estimated his probable age at just over a century.

This little incident made me reflect upon the timelessness of primitive existence, contrasting with our own obsession with history and progress and so on. It reminded me also of what I had read about the Australian aborigines and their "dream-time" past.

* * * * * * *

The jackal and the nightjar

The exploration company for which I worked as a geologist prided itself on its toughness – a sentiment not always appreciated by its employees. For example, our monthly reports had spaces to record the number of our men, or natives as the company preferred to call them, who had deserted or died during the month. This apparently enabled the company to judge how hard we were working. One month I reported seven dead, which even the company thought was excessive, until I later explained that my fourteen workers were half dead. It was then I discovered what I should have already known – that mining corporations do not have a sense of humour, at least at middle management level, although I heard afterwards that old B.B. in Joli had a chuckle over it.

When I first started work, we were not allowed the use of air photographs which enormously facilitate field work. The company decreed that we should bush-whack and observe, following parallel traverse lines laid out by compass bearings, rather than opt for easy routes which might be apparent from an air photograph. At that time also, a similar philosophy decreed that we should not have land-rovers, as did our counterparts in the government geological survey, but depend on ox-wagons for transport. We used to fume over their slowness; barring accidents, twelve miles is a good day's journey for a loaded two-wheel ox-cart, or Scotch cart as they were always called for some reason. Nevertheless, I well remember enjoying my first leisurely foray into Tonga country with one, after having been unceremoniously dumped off Chartered Exploration's lorry on the line of rail.

It was just past the end of the dry season. Last year's grass had died down, the new grass was still short, and the going was easy. The new leaves on the trees were sprouting so fast that many did not yet have chlorophyll, so that instead of appearing green they presented the shades of a British autumn. After rain in the night the early morning dew shone in the light. Many lilies were already coming into bloom in the wide moist shallow valleys known as dambos, and even gladioli were already in bud there. Eight thousand square miles of rolling wooded and savannah country on the edge of the Rift valley lay ahead of me on a reconnaissance visit. Exciting blue mountains shimmered in the far distance.

The Scotch cart which I had engaged, "sikoti carti" in the vernacular, was jointly owned by David and Daniel. Their usual employment was carrying sacks of maize to the depot in the cart, and they were glad of out of season employment. David, the larger of the two, thickset, dependable, and imperturbable, was a natural foil to Daniel's quick wit and intelligence. They were inseparable companions, both in work and play, and shared a lively sense of humour and mimicry. They were no more than about twenty-five years in age and apparently free of permanent feminine attachments, though I can remember David sulking for a time when Daniel was having a fling with a village girl. They had an introduction wherever we went and seemed to know everyone we met, and could usually tell at least one good story about them into the bargain, so travel was pleasant. One small point of friction was over birds. Daniel was amazingly adept at killing them with a catapult, but he accepted my idiosyncrasy in not wishing to see him kill any in my presence.

One afternoon we had pitched camp early under shady trees where low sandstone bluffs overhung a bend in the river course. For some distance up and down stream the river had completely dried up exposing its bed of sand. The early capricious rains had not yet resulted in a flow of water, but in one place where the sand was damp, a couple of pits quickly produced an adequate supply of reasonably clean water. An enormous lizard several feet long shared the site with us but had quickly vanished on our approach. Encouraged by the warmth of the late afternoon sun on the rocks, it reappeared from out of a fallen hollow tree and sunned itself on a ledge below the camp.

The noise of guineafowl near sundown invited me some half a mile upstream. Here there were some pools of water on the rocks in the river bed linked by a trickle of water. Much spoor included that of some large buck. After picking off an imprudently exposed, raucous sentinel guinea-cock with my two-two, I returned well satisfied with the camping place which would be our home for the next few days, and where with luck we should have plenty of meat.

Walking back to the camp in the quickly gathering dusk I nearly stepped on a nightjar, which flew up from my feet. It silently flew and wheeled and settled a short distance away between some trees. It was a male in courting plumage and trailed long white feathers like streamers from the tip of each wing. It is known, incidentally, for that reason as the pennant-winged nightjar. We had inadvertently flushed several of these birds during the day. They would wait until the very last second before flying away, and then fly only if one was about to actually step on them. Often they would appear to settle just a short distance away, but if one went to that place one would usually never be able to see them again.

I remembered David and Daniel talking about the nightjar and I had asked them to explain. David grinned in his engaging, open, shy way. "This bird, he is too proud. He knows he is very handsome." "And that is why he dies," burst in Daniel. "He is too proud. He sits there to be praised, and is caught." I explained that it was more a question of the nightjar having a justified faith in its protectively coloured plumage, and thus effectively being camouflaged. I was surprised that they didn't seem to want to accept this explanation. I knew they well understood it, but they insisted that the nightjar was "too proud".

Pleasantly tired, I read for some time that evening. We were all pleased with the camp site, and the men were talking and singing. Before thinking about turning into my camp bed, I stumbled over in starlight to where they had established themselves around their camp-fire. Unobserved in the dark, I watched by the light of the fire the same scene that they were all intently watching.

Daniel was bent down crouching on his knees, his arms tucked down beside him at the sides. His eyes were open, staring fixedly on the middle distance. He remained motionless save for slight movements of his head and trunk. Suddenly it occurred to me that he was pretending to be the nightjar. Then David approached from a direction opposite me. In a few movements he managed to simulate the nervous loping and hesitating gait of a jackal. How he managed to do this with his rather bulky frame I do not know, but as far as we spectators were concerned, he *was* a jackal. We distinctly saw his big jackal ears raise as he hesitated and sniffed. Enthralled, we watched the jackal quickly approach the nightjar and then stop. Slowly the jackal moved round the position of the nightjar. The nightjar clearly considered flight but then settled down motionless. Again round, and again, then the jackal started to run. The nightjar crouched ever closer to the ground. The jackal was now tearing round the mesmerised nightjar in a narrow circle. Suddenly the jackal cut in, and his teeth met in the shoulder of the doomed bird before our horrified eyes.

I slipped away unnoticed. How had they done it? How had David and Daniel identified themselves so completely with the two living animals? How had I come to accept, even if momentarily, that they *were* a nightjar and jackal respectively? It was a little time before I dropped off to sleep.

The next day was a long one on foot, and when a chattering honey-bird appeared in the heat of the early afternoon I was glad of an excuse for a good rest. Two or three of the men with axes followed the bird who would surely lead them to a bees' nest. While they chopped the tree down, the bird would circle and chatter, waiting impatiently for its certain reward of some of the comb. The rest of us settled down for a siesta and, hopefully, for some honey.

Their axes, by the way, were made from short lengths of car spring, much preferred to traditional native wrought iron. One end was laboriously honed into a flat blade. The other end was equally laboriously filed to a spike that was inserted into a wooden handle. The handle was quite slender, even a bit springy, no more than two feet long, and incorporated at one end a tough knot of wood into which the spiky end of the axe blade was inserted. These axes, a common design in the area, were amazingly efficient. Not for the first time, I reflected that here I was living in what was, in effect, an Iron Age farming community.

I turned to a somewhat sleepy Daniel and David. "I saw you last night." David blinked uncomprehendingly. "I saw you both when you were the nightjar and the jackal." They looked very surprised, and then Daniel laughed: "You saw him catch me?" "Yes, I tell you," I replied, "I saw it all." David had now collected himself. "Ah yes," he said, "that nightjar, he is too proud."

Denis

During the time we were prospecting for tin, Denis was the only workman to meet with an accident. The work was not inherently dangerous and the ground was good. Early rains had conveniently been enough to soften the ground and the new short grass was green. The countryside was beautiful – it was like working in a park of scattered trees. We were on the edge of a vast plateau in a pleasantly hilly zone where it met the old rift valley. The particular place where we were working straddled the route of an old track, once used by people but now mainly used by game, leading up from the rift valley to the plateau.

The first news I had of the accident was simply a message to say that Denis was sick and would not be at work that day. In this district, where an indisposition usually meant a bout of fever, such a message was a commonplace and I thought no more about it. It was not until two days later that I visited the pit where Denis had been working. To my surprise I noticed that it had been filled in before I had had a chance to examine and sample the gravel layer on the bedrock below. Also, I noticed a few stones foreign to the district were mixed with the spoil. When I questioned my headman, I was told that the place was not good and that no one must dig there.

To amplify this rather unsatisfactory statement, he presently revealed that the place was the site of an old grave. More than likely, it would have been the grave of one or more of the valley people, who were prone to chills and sickness on the long trek up through the escarpment zone to the cool plateau. Denis had unwittingly broken a taboo by disturbing the site and had reached a layer of stones that had been put on top of a corpse to prevent hyenas and jackals disinterring and devouring it, and then he had been taken sick. "Well, what's wrong with him?" I asked, scenting a small mystery. "He has hurt himself with the pick," was the unexpected reply.

That afternoon, I took the jeep to Denis's village, as I was concerned at not being able to get any clear idea of the seriousness of his injury. His workmates had reiterated that he was sick rather than physically injured.

On arrival at the village, I spoke with his wife who said that he was sick, but that he was going to see the doctor and would be better soon. Inside his kaya, when my eyes had become accustomed to the gloom, I was shocked to see the pallor of the frightened-looking face of Denis, normally a quiet but cheerful person. He was lying on the ground at the back of the round hut. I spoke with him and felt his brow. He had a high temperature, and a very nasty looking gash in his leg had not been dressed apart from a dirty looking rag. A rustle made me look round; there at the side of the hut was a black cockerel tied by its legs. I looked at Denis, querying him with my eyes. He lowered his. "The doctor has told me to come at dawn to-morrow," he said in answer to my unspoken question. "No you're not, I'm sorry," I replied, "I'm taking you to the mission hospital. You know they will look after you there."

Somewhat to my surprise, he did not demur. His wife soon got together a cooking pot, corn meal, and peppers, and we all drove the dozen or so miles to the mission. The sister, a tough, middle-aged Scots lady, raised her eyebrows significantly as she took his temperature. "Well, you're just in time. I thought you would have had the sense to bring him in straight away." She dismissed first my apologies, then my explanation, and finally me, as all being totally useless. "Has he anyone to cook for him?" (for such was the custom). "Yes, his wife is here with food." I gave some silver to the wife, who had hardly spoken a word all afternoon, in order to buy meat, and left satisfied that Denis was in competent hands. Just a part of the day's round, but not the end of the story.

That weekend I visited Denis again in the hospital with the intention of bringing him back to his village, but was startled by the shocked look that remained in his eyes. Despite treatment with modern drugs, the wound was obstinately refusing to heal, and sister was shaking her head. "It's very unusual," she said, "But there's no sign of it starting to heal. Until it does we'd better keep him here."

A few days later, I received an indignantly worded note in her firm hand, informing me that Denis had absconded. Privately, I sympathized with Denis. The sister was not exactly my idea of the epitome of feminine charm, but her note went on to say that it was essential for Denis to continue to receive treatment.

So I sent a messenger to Denis's village only to receive word that no one knew where he was. It all sounded rather strange – where else had Denis to go? Some little while later one of his fellow villagers volunteered the information that Denis was not sick any more. Passing near his village a day or two later, I called in unexpectedly and found a cheerful Denis hobbling around outside. He showed me a new poultice on his leg which was obviously healing well. I didn't recognise what the ingredients were, but I was told they were a mixture of cowdung and honey. "So you went to the doctor?" "Yes," Denis replied, "He cured the sickness. After we sacrificed the cockerel, I felt better in my mind. Then the sickness went."

The rainmaker

The deep-green budding corn stands thickly in the gardens, shading several kinds of pumpkin plants. But once again the air is dry like in the dry season. The earth too is dry and becoming harder each day and the crops are wilting. The "little winter" that can interrupt the rains for up to several weeks, though some years hardly perceptible, is long this year. As anxiety gives way to despair, the rainmaker is approached. With an eye to the tops of some towering cumulus clouds just visible far to the south, he names the day to the messenger. Immediately following the messenger's return to the village, the women begin to prepare large quantities of millet beer.

During the intervening two or three days hoeing ceases in the gardens and the children gather to play in the expectant village. Their favourite game is to trap birds. Many a handful of ground maize is cajoled from their mothers, and as they sit in the shade they whisper stories of the clever strutting yellow-eye, of the vain widow-bird fluttering his amazingly long tail feathers and hovering in the air a few feet above his several drab wives, of the always talkative black-headed finch, of the trusting blue and red waxbills, of the pink warbler who brings good fortune to the kaya (native house) where he nests, and all the others that come to the bait. Late in the afternoon the small birds scatter as two plump quail warily approach and then greedily set to and eat the maize. A furtive pull on the long string, the bent branch flies upward, and the noose tightens around the leg of one of the quail. Proudly the children carry home the petrified bright-eyed bird, and fondly the mother congratulates them, although her eyes betray her continuing uneasiness about next year's food.

The day has arrived. In the morning all are barred from the vicinity of the thicket-shrine near the big tree in the wood except those women of proved fertility. They gather there around three-quarters of a circle. The circle is completed by the rainmaker with his helper and several senior men of the village who have arranged his fee. The helper steps forward and shouts out a line of song, echoed at once by some of the older women. This is repeated and the rhythm is taken up by clapping. Soon all the women are singing. From time to time the helper shouts out another phrase, and this in turn is taken up by the women. The rainmaker stands motionless and expressionless. The rhythm changes and a subtle excitement ripples through the women. One of them runs into the middle of the large circle and dances a few steps in a small circle and then retreats. She is followed by another and yet others, so that at no time is the large circle empty. The rainmaker's eyes become glazed in a fixed stare to the south. The women continue to sing and dance as the rhythm quickens, and the chanting is now accompanied by a high-pitched cry from some of the women. Each must dance in the centre, young following the old: old wizened crones with prized ivory snuff spoons hanging from their necks and rattling around between their withered dugs flapping up and down like razor strops, plump dignified matrons, and shy young mothers with their babies tied to their backs.

The rhythm accelerates yet again. The rainmaker, a tall man dressed in black cloth and lechwe skins, maintains a look of incredible arrogance. He begins to talk rapidly, his eyes still staring and unseeing. Gradually, although the crescendo of singing is maintained, his utterances become less rapid and more separated, until eventually he sees again and is back in this world.

At a signal from the village headman all now turn to the village from where a drumming by the men now answers the singing of the women. The rainmaker is now quite recovered and takes control. With an imperiously pointed fly-whisk and intermittent blows on a reed whistle he directs the crowd, now composed of the singing women and the drumming men, to each family's house, where beer is given out in calabashes. No family is left out, and the dancing continues into the night.

Unseen, the rainmaker slips away. Though still distant, the summer sheet-lightning is nearer now and tomorrow, or perhaps the day after, plentiful rains must come. Everyone will be content.

* * * * * * *

Masuku time

In Plateau-Tonga country grows a small wild tree called the masuku which manages to produce its sweet, plum-sized, seedy fruits in the hot weather accompanying the early part of the rainy season. One can be quite sure of seeing several species of hornbills around the masuku trees at this time and hearing their bleating cries. The masuku fruit is also a special favourite of the elephant. So much so that in this season the elephant will forsake their customary haunts in the great rift valley three thousand feet below, and overnight they will follow one of their beautifully engineered trails leading through the wilderness of steep and hilly escarpment country some twenty miles or more from the valley to the plateau, specially in order to partake of the masuku.

But hornbills and elephant are not the only ones with a sweet tooth. When the masuku fruit is ripe the Tonga women travel early in the day to the known groves and gather it into enormous wicker baskets. The fruit makes excellent preserves. There is thus somewhat of an annual battle of wits between the women and the elephant: the moment the fruit anywhere is ripe, who will be there first? However, there is generally enough fruit for all, as the elephant can reach the higher branches with ease, and the damage they may do by sometimes ripping them down they repay by scattering the seeds in their droppings.

Picking the masuku fruit is fairly easy work for the women as it tends to cluster thickly enough on the lower branches. Groups of the women can be seen slowly returning in single file to their villages, heavy baskets on head, bodies swaying, in the late morning before the more oppressive heat of midday. On the way, perhaps one of the older women will start to sing – of a year when the fruit was especially plentiful, or very sweet, or of a time when they ran into elephant, or, more salaciously, of when they ran into some nice young men. With a little invention, the song and its inevitable chorus from the other women can be made to last until the village is near and the children run along the senda (path) between the scented wild-violet thickets to meet them.

And there are others who travel to masuku country. Zebra and many species of buck, followed inevitably by lion, are abundant at this time. They do not bother with the masuku fruit, but all must drink. The storms of the early rains, spectacular though they may be with their whirlwinds and thunder, bring scant and patchy rain and do little or nothing to replenish all the dried-up water courses. Both the rift valley and the plateau remain very dry at this time. But in a relatively narrow belt, where the deep rocky ravines of the escarpment have their sources at the edge of the plateau there are wide shallow valleys called dambos. Seen from the air, these appear as prominent grassy fingers amongst the gently sloping woodlands near the plateau edge. Here there is always water to be found and out-of-season crops can be grown in them.

Always water, always birds, and another native name for masuku country is the place where birds always sing. Ominously for the many species of smaller birds, goshawks, surprisingly agile for their size, are a very common bird of prey in the masuku woodlands.

For a month or so in masuku time, there is a sufficiency of meat for the numerous Tonga people who have settled this country, as their hunters join the lion in making easy killings. Occasionally a lion will attempt to find fatter prey among the cattle, and these accordingly are closely guarded in their thorn corrals at night. Some years a hunter may win glory by killing a lion, in all probability with a 19th-century muzzle-loader rather than with a spear.

This then is masuku time in Tonga country. If the previous corn harvest has been a good one, the little thatched granaries on stilts are still full enough. In the short interval between day and night, the men light their pipes and the women get on with preparing the evening meal, as a curtain of clouds, heralds of the approaching rains, is underlit by the quickly setting orange sun so that it seems that the whole western sky is aflame. In the sweet cool of the evening the nightjar swoops and trails the fantastic pennants on each wing, admired by his mate crouching expectantly in the dust. The moon of the masuku is indeed a happy time.

Something of the prevailing spirit of masuku time must have got into me, as I remember feeling very relaxed and content at the time. I seemed to have got onto good terms with the men and they were working well. I particularly remember old Chisenga who looked after the camp and did odd jobs. He was very popular with the men, as he knew the art of tempering and sharpening pickaxes which made their labouring work very much easier. He also enjoyed the tedious job of stamping out claim plates with a set of letter and number dies. Although he couldn't read, he could accurately reproduce my diagrams. He also kept the camp's woodpile stocked, and in addition kept us in fish taken from the lake. I can recall some mornings asking him what he felt like doing that day (shades of the "normal" way a white man ordered his native employees around!), secure in the knowledge that old Chisenga would be happy to find useful work to do.

I enjoyed the luxury of a settled camp for some months. I used to put out mealie meal which attracted a great variety of finches and allied birds. Blue waxbills were especially tame and would regularly come to my camp table.

During this idyllic period I had just the one visit from head office in Lusaka. It was my beloved boss again, who reserved his tenderest feelings for a young Oxford-trained geologist. The visit was chiefly memorable for his over-reaction to my having temporarily mislaid the door of my newly issued short wheel base land-rover. I had taken the door off for convenience and put it somewhere and the grass must have grown enough to cover it up. Why he should have become hysterical beat me. He never came to see me again in the bush.

I was eating well too. In the late afternoons, women would often come to the camp with plantains, eggs, milk (of dubious quality, but when boiled, a welcome change to powdered milk), a chicken or two, and mealies (corn on the cob). I can remember being harangued by some of the older women about my preference for green mealies – the ones which pop to one's fingernail and are still soft and liquid inside. They were indignant at this and told me that the hard mature mealies were much more nutritious. They were right, of course. Meal made from the mature cobs is their staple and nourishing diet, usually made into sudza (a thick porridge) eaten with a relish (a kind of soup of whatever meat and vegetables there may be available).

But there was one lithe and handsome young woman, she I will never forget, whose still brown eyes I often felt on me when she came to the camp with a load on her head and swinging hips, who indulged me by always being able to find some green mealies for me. So life was good.

* * * * * * *

The ploughing

I was only ever ill once during the nine years I worked in Africa. It was after a safari to the far side of the Kafue River. I had made a rather rash arrangement for a ferry back at a point in the plains on a big bend in the river. We had had to wait several hours with no sign of a boat and we were fearing the worst and debating what to do. Hippo were around in some number making their unexpectedly close but seemingly directionless snorting, only serving to emphasize our isolation. We were relieved when the punt-like canoe came into sight up-river. All this was not before we were caught in a heavy rain shower and wind with it. The temperature had suddenly dropped – to what would be considered a mild day in temperate latitudes! There was no shelter and we became wet and cold. A couple of days later, I became feverish with swollen glands and felt extremely weak, cold and shivery. More worrying, for some days the symptoms didn't seem to subside, and I was in no condition to travel. I can recall at this time looking at my hurricane lamp and noticing the maker's name "Chalwyn" embossed on its rim. The passing thought occurred to me that Chalwyn might be an apt nom-de-plume if I were ever to live to set down my African adventures!

While in this condition, I remember my cook Pedro appearing in the doorway of the tent one evening, looking very embarrassed and awkward. "Your friend has come to see you," he said, and vamoosed. The friend turned out to be she, the provider of green mealies. She came to the side of my bed, a straw mattress on tight thongs of bark between some solid boughs. The next thing I knew she was on the bed beside me. Somewhat ungallantly, there was nothing I could do about it but nestle close to her warm strong body and go to sleep!

I recovered within a day or so and later we became lovers. She would come, unpredictably, after sundown and slip away at dawn. There were no great protestations of love, no "romance", just a simple and natural physical act. But I came to love her and would caress her as she lay asleep beside me before falling into deep and untroubled sleep myself.

One day I was out hunting in attractive country a few miles from my camp near the edge of some cleared areas next to forest. There was a small group of kayas, a hamlet rather than a village. A woman called me over. She was the mother of my friend. She had just made some excellent changa (millet beer), and I was pressed to have rather more than I would usually have done. I had with me two quail which I had shot and I handed these over. She and her husband thanked me profusely.

I returned several times to that lovely place, a hillside clearing at the forest edge, just like I would imagine a medieval or Saxon or even earlier assart to have been like. It enjoyed a wide view over hills, and often a good healthy breeze. Her father and I would have long conversations. We used the language of Chilapalapa. Based on Xhosa, this could be described as a pigeon-Kaffir language, used throughout southern Africa, mainly as a language of command between white and black. I still remember the first phrase of the instruction book which was issued to us by the company: "A leopard has eaten my maternal aunt" – "la plume de ma tante" in another continent! Nevertheless, we found we could convey anything we wanted to talk about through the medium of this Chilapalapa. I remember once I hesitatingly expressed my feelings of misgiving at what I thought was my irresponsible behaviour with his daughter. I mentioned that one day I would have to leave. He smiled. "I know," he replied simply.

My men and I happened to pass that same way on starting a short safari. There had been some fairly determined rain on several days the preceding week. The ground no longer had the appearance of red dust but was now a brown moist earth. She was ploughing the garden – a rectangular, nearly square, plot with sides no more than about forty or fifty yards long. Pulling the massive wooden plough were two heavily yoked and clumsy oxen. A young boy was in front trying, rather ineffectually, to turn them round at the heads. The plough was essentially a pointed and slightly tilted scraper with no pretensions of a mouldboard. One direction had already been ploughed, and she was now ploughing again at right angles. Her father and some others were watching with obvious approval.

Out of bravado, or was it perhaps something deeper, I felt impelled to go and take the plough myself and follow the oxen. It was unbelievably hard work. She came to help me. We stumbled and struggled together, side my side, she naked to the waist, both of us and the oxen bathed in sweat. The good earth smelled sweet, sweeter than us I dare say. After some half dozen rows I was exhausted and gave up. Her father was smiling. So were my men, not unkindly. I remember the look in her father's eyes to this day.

A fuller realisation only came to me later, although I find it hard to express. I would say that he knew, and I know now, that at that moment I had been close, closer probably than I would ever be again, to the Earth Goddess, well antedating Jehovahs and sundry other man-made Gods. I realised also that I had been briefly transported back in time four or five millennia to the Neolithic. Truly, "In the sweat of thy brow shalt thou eat bread."

Later that day my arms and back and legs felt as if I had been tortured on the rack. I marvelled again at the great strength in her lithe body. My African nickname changed yet again from "the bwana who leans forward as he walks" (a reflection, no doubt, of my early impatience) and, later, "the bwana who talks softly" (I must have relaxed) to, quite simply, "the ploughman". I would like to think that, although typically ironic, it was not unkindly intended.

At length I had to leave, after delaying as long as I possibly could. She slipped away at dawn on the day of my departure and I never saw her again. I have never forgotten her and she has not forgotten me. For after forty years she is still with me in my dreams. Only recently, we were in difficult jungle. Ahead of us were glimpses of a beautiful white city built on the bank of a majestic river. We were trying to get there, but the going was so desperately hard I felt like giving up, but she would have none of it. She was confident of the way and although our progress was slow and difficult she urgently insisted that I follow her.

Perhaps we westerners try too hard to put things into words which are there all the time deep down in our psyche. Perhaps at times we feel the need of poetry or great music to express things, as in the line "the eternal feminine leads us onwards" taken up in Mahler's Eighth. All I can say is that African woman became and remains for me the admirable personification of Earth-Goddess, whom it is fashionable these days to call Gaia.

* * * * * * *

The plain

This is a brief account of a visit to one of the plains of central Africa. The plain is flooded each year by the great river, whose waters do not subside until the dry season is far advanced. Between the shrinking lagoons left by the flood the new short grass is green and sweet. Multitudes of birds come to the lagoons where fish are trapped, and multitudes of animals come to the plain to graze – and some to kill.

Carrying some bulky but carefully selected nkuni (firewood), for there are no trees at all on the great plain, I camped alone one evening at an indeterminate spot selected just to be as far as possible from any standing water. Nevertheless, when nightfall came the mosquitoes were worse than I had ever known. Only crouched over the smoke of my tiny cooking fire was there some brief respite from them. There was no moon but I could see quite well by starlight. The hemisphere of stars was complete and brilliantly bright, such as I have never known before or since, slashed by the opal of the Milky Way. The Great Bear was just falling below the northern horizon and in the other direction the Southern Cross had turned over and it too was descending. Direction therefore was easy to ascertain but the plain itself was immense and featureless. I fixed a mosquito net inside my tiny bivouac tent and after killing most of the mosquitoes I slept soundly in my light sleeping bag.

It is unlikely, I think, that anyone of this generation would be able to see what I saw on waking that misty dawn. At a range of 120 yards were zebra in a complete circle around me, gazing inwards without fear at the strange sight of me emerging from the small tent and preparing a hurried breakfast of mealiemeal porridge. A random rifle shot could hardly have missed hitting one, although such was not my intention, and indeed I had no firearms with me. Among the zebra, but mostly further away, were large numbers of red lechwe, a large buck with attractive spiral horns.

As the sun rose, and the dim greys of early dawn changed to technicolour, and the sky changed quickly from grey to yellow to faint blue, and visibility improved, the watching animals dispersed. Now it was possible to see uninterruptedly across the plain. Everywhere there were groups of grazing animals, mainly red lechwe, their backs glinting in the low sun – I suppose there may have been some tens of thousands within my view. They formed a pattern of motionless or gently moving herds, their serenity contrasting with the prancing gait of an occasional wildebeest.

In the cool and pleasant morning air I started for the river, noting my general direction by the sun. The river was restrained now at this time of year to its proper channel some five or six miles away. Occasional white objects proved to be cleaned bones and it was not long before I saw a newly-killed zebra carcass closely surrounded by maribou storks and vultures. As I approached the vultures were reluctant to leave and the last one hopped out of the animal's stomach only a few yards in front of me and slowly took to the air after a long series of ungainly flapping hops. The poor zebra had very probably been a victim of lion in the night. Zebra, generally old, sick, or lame individuals, universally meet this fate, and depend for their collective survival on their ability to breed faster than the lion can kill them. I have been told that lion when not hunting may walk quite close to zebra without the latter showing fear. Only when the zebra recognise the near grunting cough of a hungry lion are they afraid.

Nearer the river, the almost imperceptible undulations in the surface of the plain were revealed by numerous lagoons of shallow water where trapped fish were the prey of thousands of birds that rose in screaming white clouds from each lagoon as I skirted it. Taking a quieter and more distant look at one lagoon through field glasses I watched the numerous white and yellow-billed egrets, ibis and spoonbills interspersed with larger black-headed herons, crested cranes, marabou storks and pelicans, all busily feeding.

A gorged fish eagle with brilliant brown, black, and white plumage regarded me with cruel eyes as I approached it slowly on the ground to within ten paces before disdainfully taking off in powerful flight. This was easily the closest I have ever been to such a majestic bird of prey in the wild.

Overawed by what I had seen, I commenced the long plod back. A surreal effect was caused by the horizon all round me becoming completely diffused and lost in mirages, so that I seemed to carry a little clear zone with me as I walked on in the increasing heat of the day.

Eventually the mirages subsided and I was intercepted by an African game-ranger, who was very surprised that I was alone. He was a chubby happy man whose long-sighted eyes traversed the horizon as we spoke. He told me that he had over two hundred successful convictions for poaching that year alone. He clearly liked his work of attempting to preserve the animals of the plains from otherwise certain eventual extermination. But he was now pleading with the white game officer in overall charge to be transferred far away, as he knew that some of the poachers had sworn to murder him after unsuccessfully trying to bribe him. In a land where protein food was always chronically short, population increasing, efficient rifles coming to be more widely owned, and road transport available, fortunes could be made by the sale of zebra and other meat at a shilling a pound.

"You see," he explained, "It is not these people we are after." He pointed to a distant group of people, the only other humans I was to see that day. Their steady course across the plain converged with and presently crossed our own. They proved to be two men carrying on their shoulders a long spear and an old muzzle-loader respectively, presumably for protection, followed by five brightly clothed women carrying loads on their heads, all in single file, and travelling at quite a smart pace. After just one glance at us and a shouted greeting, they intently pursued their bee-line across the plain without further speaking, like a silent convoy on the ocean. "These people do not kill many animals and, anyway, they have been hunting animals for a long time. We do not prosecute these people."

It was nearly sunset before I rejoined the scrub and savannah land bordering the plain, not before adding to my sightings of the day a noble sable buck, a large herd of eland, and some giraffe. I fell asleep almost at once after making camp and cooking, but not before reflecting that I had been near to creation and my Creator that day.

I had penetrated back in time to before mankind. It was an experience which my poor words cannot adequately convey, although I use them here in an attempt to share a privilege that was granted me. Unusually, I had been alone, and this no doubt had accentuated my impressions.

Later, I realised that the day marked the zenith of my "African awakening". No other continent could have been so gracious to me. I once read that a Celt can be defined as a person who uses their dreams to understand the past. Alas, I have never been so skilled. But Africa did the job for me. Unforgettably.

For some time, my symphony of African experiences remained pleasant on the whole, especially my time in the Zambezi rift valley itself, of which more anon. Sadly, however, as I shall also try to document, increasingly jarring notes were to creep into the score, eventually to create such a discord that, with great sadness, I had to escape.

* * * * * * *

The Valley

To those of us who ever worked in the Zambezi Concession, the "Valley" signified one thing alone – the Zambezi rift valley. It was always a place of excitement and mystery, fancifully akin perhaps to Conan Doyle's *Lost World*. But whereas the Lost World was up on an isolated plateau, the rift valley was an isolated piece of primeval Africa some three thousand feet down, along which flowed the Zambezi. It was alas to be the scene of tragedy, of which more anon.

Rift valleys are almost unique to Africa. They are places where the earth's crust has dropped down in elongate blocks, typically up to hundreds of miles long and some thirty or so miles wide. Where they are geologically young, the fault boundaries at their sides are well-defined, obvious, and steep. Where old, like the Zambezi rift valley, although just as deep, the place of a sharp boundary is taken by a wide zone of very steep, highly dissected country of ridges and ravines known as the escarpment zone, itself up to fifteen miles wide. The Zambezi escarpment zone has to be seen to be believed. It would be hard to find fifty yards of level ground in it. Furthermore, it is completely uninhabited. So complete is the separation of plateau from valley that even major rivers that flow from the plateau through the escarpment zone and then across the broad rift-valley floor to join the Zambezi have different names on the plateau and in the valley. For example, the Monzuma and Nzimu of the plateau become the Zongwe and Jimini, respectively, in the valley.

My longest stay in the Zambezi rift valley came about in a curious manner. A large part of it was about to be flooded by the huge artificial lake backed up by the Kariba Dam. The company for which I worked had decided, in its wisdom, that as the valley was included in the area for which it had been given (yes, *given*) concessionary rights to mineral exploration, the company should be *reimbursed* by the colonial government for the value of any mineral deposits that might have been present in that part of that valley which was to be inundated! Wonderful – cash for nothing! Some one in Head Office had excelled themselves. The company's cutting edge in this wonderful scheme was me! My job was to do a reconnaissance and quickly outline any potential for theoretical mineral deposits that would never be mined anyway! I could not in all honesty take this project seriously and treated it to some extent as a paid holiday. In any event, the same job had already been well done in outline by an excellent government geologist some years previously. I remember discussing all this with Nigel Baird over a beer or two in Lusaka. He was horrified at my "disloyal" attitude to my employers!

The Zambezi rift valley was indeed a different world to the plateau. It was thinly inhabited by distinct tribal groups known collectively as the Valley-Tonga, who practised hunter-gathering together with primitive agriculture on the banks of the Zambezi and near one or two of its major tributaries. Typically, they would cultivate the rich alluvium left behind on flood terraces on the flanks of the rivers as the latter subsided after annual floods. Traditionally the women used to wear a modest grass skirt, the men rather less, but nowadays most of the women wore loose garments of a cheap black cloth and most men sported khaki shorts and shirts, usually in a ruinous condition.

Separating their villages were considerable distances of untouched bush. Some of it was savannah with many species of acacia. Some was thickly wooded. Parts had a semi-arid flora including many varieties of thorns, together with aloes and grotesque giant baobab trees. According to native legend, the baobab tree was the one that the devil, jealous of the creator who had given him just this one species to plant, had planted upside down for spite with its roots in the air. Sucking the seeds from the big seed-pods of the baobab is remarkably thirst-quenching.

Working in the valley was thus like being in an enormous variegated park, one could almost say an Eden. Bird and animal life were abundant, although of course not as immediately obvious as on the treeless plain I have described above. Among the birds were a great many colourful species of weavers, rollers, and bee-eaters, together with lovebirds and paradise flycatchers that I had never seen on the plateau.

I remember often surprising families of wild boar that would go off with a tremendous crashing through the bush, or quite large herds of impala that would escape by gracefully covering the ground in extraordinarily long hops. Elephant were abundant. They came right up to our camp one night and politely turned aside, and we never even heard them! Once, travelling upwind, although we knew we were very close to elephant on account of warm droppings, we happened to get right amongst a herd of them before we or they realised it. This sounds crazy, but we were walking at times in an "elephant warren" of trails in very tall grass. It was the middle of the day, and the elephant had been quietly resting among trees and the long grass. The first we knew was the sounds of their tummies rumbling. They went off in a great rush, one passing close to me.

Due to a general shortage of available water, once we were forced to camp not far from a family of lion who had their young in a ravine with a stream close to the edge of the valley floor. As there were no reports of any man-eaters on the go, it was OK. We noted their spoor coming close to our camp site in the night, so they obviously knew about us and tolerated us, but we were careful to keep our distance from their actual lair.

We were always careful to give buffalo a very wide berth also. Although they give the appearance of quietly grazing like cattle, the bulls are wily and unpredictable. Once or twice we passed a herd where the bulls had already started to form a defensive phalanx between us and the remainder of the herd. No sane person tangles with a charging buffalo, still less one that might have been wounded, so we left heroics to others.

Talking of buffalo reminds me of buffalo bean, common in places in the escarpment ravines and in the valley, but never found on the plateau. This is a climbing pea, the pods of which are covered in short glossy rich-brown hairs like buffalo skin, hence the name. The trouble is that when ripe, as was the case with us in the dry season, the hairs are easily dislodged, even by the slight draught caused by one's walking by. On contact, they set up an intense skin irritation which is long-lasting and ten times worse than nettles. If one inadvertently walks into them or even near them, the irritation is appalling, quite enough to disrupt one's whole day. One inexperienced geologist I knew was severely nettled by his first encounter with buffalo bean and, not knowing what it was, ran away through yet more buffalo bean, and ended up hysterical, having scratched his whole chest and stomach and arms until they were raw and bloody. He had to be treated in hospital for both the physical and mental trauma. Apparently, his men had not had time to alert him before he took off. We treated buffalo bean very, very gingerly!

Once I visited a most amazing and isolated part of the rift valley system. What had happened in the geological past was that complex earth movements had resulted in a subsidiary small fault-bounded rift valley parallel to the major valley. The only practicable way into it was through a gorge that had cut steeply through some intervening mountains for some miles. There was a reasonable game trail through the gorge in places, but in several narrow places we were obliged to wade in the river bed and climb some minor rock obstacles, as presumably did any travelling animals that were sufficiently agile. The going was slow, and we were overtaken by darkness and had to camp in the gorge on a section of game trail.

That night was memorable for two things. The first was a total eclipse of the moon which I had known was due. I had been a little naughty and told one of the carriers who was flagging that the moon would cry for him that night. When eclipse came, the moon became a weird coppery colour and the women started wailing (I had some women carriers on this occasion – they tended to be tougher and harder working than the men!). I was sleeping at one end of our motley caravan which was spread out along the trail, and my second memory was later that night waking up uneasily to find myself looking at a hyena just three yards away. The beast hesitated for some while before shuttling off. Hyenas have been known to bite off half a sleeping man's face. Their teeth are fearsome – once I had an enamelled metal plate that had been taken by a hyena in the night and completely bitten through.

The following days we explored our "mini-valley", which had just one village in it. Now all villages are supposed to be visited annually by a government district officer. This one had not seen one or indeed any white man for at least twenty years. When I offered a shilling for a chicken, a fair price in the valley, the coin was examined and then indignantly thrown to the ground. It couldn't be British money – it had an umfazi (woman) on it! Britain would not have a woman on a coin. At best the coin was Portuguese money of doubtful value! So I had to explain that King George was dead and our gracious sovereign was now his daughter Queen Elizabeth. This was 1957! But the king should have taken another wife and had sons! The seller of the chicken was only mollified when I offered a canvas sample bag for the chicken in lieu of the shilling about which he obviously still had reservations. The headman used an exact biblical phrase to describe his village – a land flowing with milk and honey. Curiously, there were no tsetse-fly (the carrier of sleeping sickness to both cattle and humans) and cattle flourished, unlike much of the valley, and there were indeed many wild bees. The villagers were a remarkably self-sufficient bunch and apparently rarely travelled away from home. Low population pressure and a good supply of water meant adequate food resources. We lingered several days in our "Shangri La", having made good friends with its native inhabitants. It gives me pleasure to record that they were unaffected by the events I shall describe later.

As a postscript to my ten-week valley sojourn, I visited the construction site of Kariba Dam. Access to the actual site was restricted, so with a few of my men, we rolled up in our battered land-rover just behind a large construction vehicle. When the gateman lifted the barrier for it, we carried on after the lorry without stopping to explain, and just gave an airy wave to the gateman as if we were legitimates in a hurry. It worked. At sundown, I spoke to some of the Italian workers who had just come off their twelve-hour shift and explained that we were sightseers, quite literally gatecrashers! They could not have been more welcoming, found billets for my men and myself, and insisted on giving us food and beer. We conversed, perforce, quite fluently in the lingua franca of the dreadful Chilapalapa.

They took us all down to the river site later that evening, and we walked across a temporary suspension footbridge over the Zambezi in the moonlight just below the site of the dam. I was amazed to realise that, after letting the Zambezi flow right over the partly built dam next rainy season, they intended to race the river's rise the following rainy season and complete the four hundred foot high dam.

Later, I sat alone and meditated on the mighty Zambezi, flooding each wet season over the great plains of Barotseland. Then falling in a huge mass of water into a giant chasm a mile long and over three hundred feet deep to form Mosi-ua-Tunya (the "smoke that thunders" – Victoria Falls). Then on through the great gorges below the Falls for some 60 miles. Then along the floor of the great rift valley proper for another 200 miles to Kariba. The mighty river was bridged only once between where I was sitting and the Victoria Falls, by a graceful arched bridge thrown across the gorge actually just downstream of the Falls. The man who had it built was a dreamer, who had come to the warm clean air of southern Africa dying of TB with just a few months to live. He survived and, among other things, had a country named after him. I am not sure whether his command to site the bridge where the spray of the Falls would sometimes reach it was all that practical! At least, in a sense his bridge paid homage to the river. But it seemed an act of arrogance, almost outrage, to harness the river at Kariba.

Later still that evening we sat out with the Italians who sang resonantly in harmony in the warm African night many thousands of miles from their homeland. I must say I had to admire them, but my overall feelings on the eve of departure from the Valley, my Eden, were mixed.

* * * * * * *

Jailos

I suppose that we all have a sense of humour. Its nature is often a good guide to the personality of its owner. Few of us, however, have a capacity for sustained comic invention. I suspect that this often depends on a philosophy of life and on powers of observation deeper than those that may be credited to their possessor. One of the most humorous persons I have ever met was a man who once worked for me as a labourer and carrier for one shilling and three pence a day.

I cannot recall the actual occasion when Jailos signed on at my Zambezi rift-valley camp and indeed his physical appearance was not remarkable at first sight. He was of average height with perhaps a slight tendency to plumpness, most marked in a rounded face and thick neck. I would say he was stronger than average, and conspicuous after one had known him but a short while for gentleness and good manners, notable even among the likeable tribal people of the Valley. He wore an agreeable expression compounded with elements of doubt and pensiveness. Whether this was natural or worn as a mask I couldn't say. I never heard him laugh out loud, and his rare delightful smile, although broad, was fleeting. I recall that occasions for this smile might be when I looked up from plotting the day's work, or from trying to find out why the land-rover wouldn't go, and unexpectedly find myself under his observation. More generally, he would permit himself to smile when the men, having tumbled to the point of one of his long stories, were rolling with laughter.

One facet of Jailos that served to draw us together was his considerable knowledge of plants. I discovered that he knew much more than the others about them and about their medicinal uses. I used to carry a book on the subject around with me. Jailos always professed to be amazed at the book's erudition, generally before himself adding a few details that the book hadn't got. Furthermore, he had a keen naturalist's eye for the rarity or oddity, and also an appreciation of natural beauty unrelated to practical necessities and uses. This was something he didn't speak about, but I sometimes noticed him gazing intently at a hillside, or a tree, or a riverside modelled by the warm light of the setting sun. If one asked what exactly he could see, the reply accompanied by a faint smile would be non-committal. Several times he accompanied me pottering around after the formal day's work was over and I was always very glad of his company.

In an odd sort of a way Jailos was a leader with a wide range of power which fortunately never overlapped with that of my headman, Bonwero. Bonwero was a bit of a tyrant whose autocracy I relied upon at times but secretly deplored. I remember noticing that when Bonwero transmitted instructions to the men, they expectantly looked to Jailos, and were visibly encouraged by his air of stoical acceptance!

Safaris were somewhat of a trial to Jailos, who seemed better designed for contemplation than for movement. He often seemed to end up with the bulkiest load of the many carefully partitioned out by Bonwero at dawn on the first day of safari. Jailos always lagged a little, and at our resting places the sight of Jailos slowly marching in was unforgettable. He maintained that the weight of the load was compressing and shortening his neck, and making it thicker at the same time. His physical appearance indeed lent weight to this hypothesis, further enhanced by his wearing a choker neckerchief. His plaintive voice bewailing his relatively shorter rests than the others, and the sight of him surreptitiously feeling the top of his head with one hand and his neck with the other never failed to put fresh heart into the men.

I have a photograph of a group of us on safari and indeed it was seeing this that triggered these memories of Jailos. In the forefront of the picture is Bonwero, standing at attention and shouldering my rifle. One was never quite allowed to forget that he had once been a corporal in the King's African Rifles (although he had had the good sense to desert when war began). Behind him, untidily spread over a large rock outcrop in a dry gorge, are eight or so men, momentarily and uncharacteristically self-conscious, At the very rear is Jailos with his back to the camera; he is looking upstream, his round head a little to one side, silently but eloquently managing to convey his ever-present misgivings.

In areas of much game and wildlife many stories would be told around the evening campfire – of a man-eating lion who, daring the blaze of the fire, would snatch away a man, or of the elephant or hippo who, taking a dislike to the embers of a campfire, would charge and scatter them and trample the soft human bodies nearby, or of the watching hyena who, with one snap of its jaws, could bite off the face of a sleeper. Remote as all these and other possibilities were, any fears would finally be quelled by Jailos. Jailos had the notion that he would be the first to be eaten because he was the fattest and sweetest. Finding the places near the fire taken, he would perforce sleep head in blanket protestingly on the periphery. It was no uncommon thing in the night to hear a hyena's cry followed by one or two muffled words from Jailos and an explosion of merriment from the men. In short, Jailos was invaluable.

Regrettably, I never understood a tenth of all Jailos used to say in the vernacular, but I do know his love-life figured prominently in many of his plaintive discourses in camp, when the sound of his monotonous voice would be broken by that of uncontrollable laughter from his listeners. Jailos seemed to lack an element of male aggressiveness and dominance, perhaps overly expected of men in Tonga tribal society, and the themes of many of his stories – Jailos maintained that he was severely henpecked by his wife – seemed to strike a chord among the men. I should perhaps add that Jailos appeared to be happily married to a handsome and capable woman, to whom he modestly introduced me with a deprecatory smile on the one occasion when we passed by his village.

But Jailos's greatest difficulty of all lay in understanding the curious ways of the white man. Nevertheless, he had considerable respect for their kindness and generosity as the following story of his, told in Chilapalapa around an evening campfire, mainly I suspect for my benefit, will show.

One time, Jailos related, with no money in his pocket, he had made the long journey on foot to see the capital city, Lusaka, his first and only visit. Arriving late one evening with nowhere to sleep, and not having been able to locate fellow tribesmen, he had settled for the night in a shop doorway. It was uncomfortable and draughty and Jailos couldn't sleep when about eleven o'clock a white man, beautifully dressed in a clean, pressed, khaki uniform (Jailos here cast a glance at my own well-worn clothing) came along and asked him what he was doing there. Jailos explained that he had nowhere to sleep, whereupon the white man took him in his smart land-rover straight to his own house. Here Jailos was given a room of his own, small but clean, with a serviceable bunk to sleep on. The white man had locked the door and assured him that he would sleep there safely until morning.

Indeed, so soundly did Jailos sleep that he had to be woken up next morning by a uniformed African servant who brought him a large hot bowl of his favourite corn porridge. After this breakfast and a rest, his kind friend of the previous evening had taken him to a large cool panelled room, where Jailos was introduced to an older white man dressed in very fine civilian clothes. This man, after enquiring whether Jailos had any papers or work and receiving negative replies, invited him to stay on for another seven days with full board in return for work, not an unreasonable arrangement at all.

So, each day for a week, Jailos enjoyed a pleasant stroll to different parts of the city with a dozen or so other men who were able to give him a lot of interesting information. Wherever they went they had an escort of two uniformed men armed with rifles to protect them from any possible danger. Jailos recalled with pride that one day he was allowed to carry the rifle of one of their escorts who was feeling tired. The work was not arduous (Jailos sighed and felt his neck), usually grass-cutting with long curved metal blades swinging in time to a song sung by one of their company. They took it in turns to sing, improvising couplets about the white men and women who were passing by, trying to characterise each in the fewest words possible, facetiously, unkindly, or sympathetically, according to their appearance and mannerisms. One was very good at it and so earned relatively longer intervals of rest and often attracted an appreciative native audience who laughed and applauded and gave them all food and fruit. They enjoyed frequent rests to observe the coming and going of this new city, arising and growing unexplained and alien out of the African savannah. Each night Jailos slept comfortably after a good meal in the same small room of his own, always locked against possible thieves and with the additional security of a night-watchman.

Jailos understood that if he were to stay longer he would be given new clothes with an attractive pattern like those which some of his workmates had, but not even this further example of the white man's generosity could tempt him. The fact was that towards the end of the week, Jailos realised he wanted to go home. He had seen enough of the city to know that he preferred life with his own people in the rift valley.

He was not looking forward to the long hot walk back, when early in the morning the white man who had befriended him in the shop doorway unexpectedly appeared and offered to arrange a lift home for him in a truck. As he boarded, along with other people from his tribe and from neighbouring areas for the one hundred and fifty mile journey, again protected by a uniformed guard of two men with rifles, his white friend asked him if he had learned his lesson. Jailos, kneeling and with his two hands cupped together in the traditional token of respect, expressed his warm thanks as he had enjoyed a most interesting and pleasant stay and had indeed learned very much. Although he really had no great desire to return to the city, he added, as was only polite, that he hoped he might return and see his white friend again. His sorrow on parting, probably for ever, was increased when he noticed sudden signs of deep emotion in his white friend, who flushed and trembled and appeared to say something like "cheeky Kaffir" although he, Jailos, clearly could not have understood him correctly. Such a cultivated and kind gentleman would never dream of using such language said Jailos, glancing in my direction.

This was a little story, one of many, told some years ago now around a campfire in the Zambezi rift valley by Jailos, an illiterate Bantu tribesman, a man whom I am happy and proud to remember as a good companion.

* * * * * * *

The Mvuradona Mountains

One of my last lingering memories of the Valley at that time was looking across to an imposing high plateau-like massif of bare red-brown mountains overlooking the rift valley on its southern side. Two years later, by chance, I was to visit these mountains on foot, approaching them from the tableland country of Southern Rhodesia (now Zimbabwe). Their attractive name means "mountains of the morning dew". They lie some distance beyond the most northerly tobacco farms near Sipolilo and beyond any pretence of a road. I imagine they are still very rarely visited.

A small party of us explored these lonely mountains in the dry season. We slept out in our sleeping bags on this safari, as although the nights were cool, there was no possibility of rain. The mountains lived up to their name, however, and the mornings were in fact pretty moist with dew! One evening just at sunset I remember being puzzled by a phenomenon in the sky that I had never seen before. I then realised I was watching one of the new earth satellites. In its measured passage across the sky it intermittently reflected the sun, which had just set where we were. Somehow, it only seemed to emphasize our isolation. I slept at peace with my gun by my side and my ridgeback lying across my feet, and I couldn't give a damn for anyone.

On the mountains there was always a cooling breeze and any stray skudding clouds seemed to rise up over the edge of the massif and tear themselves into shreds and dissolve as they crossed. Lying on the flat-topped summit of the highest mountain after a steep climb, one could imagine oneself alone on the roof of the world, with only sky around and no other land in sight and only birds for company. I remember watching there a display of aerial acrobatics, the participants being a lanner falcon and two falcons of another species that came stooping at it out of the sun.

On the lip of the summit plateau near its highest edge some low crags had shed reddish-purple boulders of weathered serpentine onto a steep slope. Several unusual plants, drawing water mainly from the dew, had colonised this rocky place, combining to make a spectacular natural rock garden. A lonely aloe nodded its red spiky flower head at the top.

Also not far from the summit plateau there was a grassy hollow with a spring whose beautifully clear and refreshing water trickled only a short distance in a little stream before disappearing underground. It was regularly visited in the short dawns and twilights by small buck, whose faint tracks were the only obvious signs of larger land animals in this lonely place.

Seemingly untouched by the hand of man, the mountains revealed in fact some indications of a human history. On the ascent, we had discovered a small overhanging cavern partly masked by tumbled boulders. From inside the cavern the fallen rocks framed a view of yet another range of red serpentine mountains far to the west rising above an immense tangle of wooded granite-kopje country. On the inner walls of the cave, the little Bushmen hunters of times past had recorded their hunting successes in red, black, and brown paintings of porcupine, kudu, monkey, hippo, elephant, etc. We were to discover several more sites of rock paintings nearby. Some of the animal paintings were deliberately out of proportion but they were always executed in such a way as to marvellously portray the identity, the spirit, of the animal. At one site, groupings of ticks in units of seven were obviously counting something – but what? – phases of the moon? In a couple of sites the Bushman artists of long ago had included scenes of groups of people dancing, some of the dancers wearing head-dresses resembling an antelope's head.

Centuries ago, these mountains had also been a landmark for fever-wracked Portuguese expeditions, desperately searching for El Dorado in long deadly journeys from the Indian Ocean coast up the low-lying and unhealthy Zambezi valley. Their records spoke of a fort built in the area by would-be conquistadores who had died like flies from fever. Not until white explorers made the longer but far healthier journey from the other direction northwards over the high Southern Rhodesian plateau were any of the adjacent highlands ever successfully settled by white people. Before exploring the Mvuradona, I had been taken on a flight with some historians on a plane belonging to my company with the objective of trying to locate this old Portuguese fort from the air. It was a futile although incredibly scenic quest. On foot, however, in a wooded area containing an unusual species of palm tree below a pass past the Mvuradona to the plateau, we did come across some traces of foundations of a large earthen structure that just might have been the ruins of the fort in question. If so, it was a monument of pathos, not of conquest. I thought it as moving as the well-known ruins of Zimbabwe.

Now, on a prospecting safari, I experienced an overwhelming and intense desire not to find any minerals that might lead to the tranquillity of this place ever being disturbed – not the first time that I had entertained such disloyal thoughts!

PART II SEEDS OF DISILLUSION

Red dust of Africa,
So fine and sweet,
Softly you have blown into my soul.

Every grain a memory,
From so many lands,
Africa, now I can see you whole.

A picture of colour,
Dancing and mirth,
Dignity, sorrow, and pain.

Be now true to yourself,
Be wise as old,
And too proud to suffer again.

Town

Although I enjoyed my life in the bush and lived well and comfortably within my field allowance of ten shillings per day, I must admit it was pleasant to get up to town occasionally and meet other geologists, typically at the end of a month for two or three days. Town, of course, was Lusaka, the capital of Northern Rhodesia.

At that time Lusaka consisted of a fairly long road parallel to the railway line. The road, somewhat optimistically, was called Cairo Road. This had reflected, I suppose, the dream of Rhodes and others of a continuous north-south belt of imperial red on the map for the six-thousand mile length of Africa.

Curiously, those restless and rapacious French had entertained a similar notion of a continuous belt of French Africa from east to west, across the region of the Sahel. Now it is a matter of simple geometry to appreciate that the two must intersect. They did, in 1898 at Fashoda on the Nile, when a French column under Marchand and a British one under Kitchener came face to face, each having beaten up the natives en route. After some comic-opera manoeuvrings and diplomacy, war (at least, between Europeans) was narrowly averted and a compromise reached. For many years afterwards, atlases showed the Sudan not in red, not in yellow, but in a diagonally striped pattern of the two! Poor Africa. Did she really need us?

Anyway, to get back to town. Cairo Road was paved with a narrow strip of tar, flanked by generous expanses of mud on each side. The mud was flanked in turn on one side by uneven wooden sidewalks whose haphazard development had been left largely to the efforts of the individual Indian, Greek, and Syrian traders whose shops lined the road. We used to gather near sundown at the Lusaka Hotel, where you could lounge on the verandah in easy cane chairs, put your boots up on the rail, drink beer, and tell tall stories. Suitably refreshed, we would go inside to eat as much as we could of an excellent five-course menu for five shillings and sixpence. For some reason, the manager always seemed anxious to shunt us into a corner of the dining room, but the African waiters knew us and always spoiled us and we let them in to some of our exploits. Suitably watered and fed, we would then stagger to Lusaka's top attraction, the cinema, to see an old movie – and maybe even hear it too if the rain was not too heavy on the tin roof.

Reporting in at the office was always a bit of a trial. We had changed from having an excellent secretary and a most appalling boss (the one who tended to become hysterical over such trivial matters as my mislaying a land-rover door), to a penny-pinching humourless secretary and a nice boss who treated us to unlimited quantities of whisky and lemonade.

This boss was the most accomplished and versatile fellow I've ever met. I began to keep notes of some of the things he modestly told us about himself on various occasions. He had been a Cambridge triple blue and Scottish international and had three doctor's degrees. He was a mathematical genius and could have been another Einstein if he had stuck to maths. When President of the Cambridge University Union he wore a monocle and spats. He had done research chemistry on radium using one-tenth of a milligram before switching to geology. He and Rutherford spent a night in Bow Street jail together after they had pulled a London policeman's helmet down over his eyes. He was also musical – at the age of twelve he had played a four-manual organ for a whole service in Glasgow cathedral without music. In the first world war, he had joined the Flying Corps and been mentioned in dispatches three times and won the French Croix de Guerre. Sometimes he landed frozen stiff and had to be lifted out of his open cockpit by crane. He was one of only two men in the southern hemisphere able to analyse chrome. He had a gift for languages and was fluent in French, German, and Afrikaans (South African Dutch), although he was too modest to demonstrate this ability to us. Despite being a poor swimmer he had once repeatedly dived in to deep water and rescued four people in succession from a car that had fallen off a pontoon at a Transvaal river crossing. He once broke his neck and lost only one day from work. During the second world war, he was in overall charge of demolitions in the Middle East. Once he stood for half an hour near a bull elephant eighteen feet tall while working in the Zambezi valley in a temperature of 150°. He had an ivory tusk in his room belonging to an elephant that had killed a native standing just beside him two years previously. He once delivered twenty babies in three days; this had put him off the medical profession, although he had first come out to Africa as a medical missionary. He was also a "hereditary freeman" (whatever that may have meant) of the City of Glasgow. He could have looked forward to a private investment income of 4000 Pounds a year (a sizable sum then, equivalent to more than four times my salary at the time) but a drunken father had lost it all gambling. He had been president of the South African mountaineering club just prior to Smuts.

He rather spoilt it all when he told me one day that he had never had an argument with his wife in thirty years of marriage, because at that moment I suddenly began to doubt his veracity!

Granted that Africa somehow always seemed to accentuate a person's inherent weaknesses and strengths, why oh why do we have to lie to others – and to ourselves? Why can't we let the world take us for what we are? Why can't we accept ourselves for what we are?

Having eventually satisfied the miserable and suspicious secretary by means of some creative accounting on my expense sheet, and having taken as much as I could stand of the boss's whisky and conversation, I often used to take myself off to see old Tom.

Tom lived the other side of the railway track in a small hut. He was a pioneer who had become well known in the Territory as a recruitment agent for the South African mines, and had won a reputation among Africans for honesty and fair dealing. Poor Tom walked with a permanent limp acquired when his brother shot him in the leg during an argument over an African woman. He used to kick Africans off the sidewalk in Lusaka if they got in his way as he limped along. This used to embarrass me if I were with him, but I noticed that when they turned round to remonstrate, their faces turned to smiles when they recognised him. Tom was always interested in my doings. In fact, he was the only person I felt I could confide anything to. Over cheap Cape brandy in his kaya, he himself would also loosen up and tell (possibly true!) stories of the good old days, including one period in his youth running copra, ivory, and slave girls up the east coast in a schooner to Mombasa and Zanzibar.

Some white people and all the wives considered Tom disreputable and would have nothing to do with him, but there was no pretence in the man. I liked him for it.

* * * * * * *

Njara

It became difficult to imagine camp life without bossboy Njara. Tall, lean and mean, he could be relied upon to settle most labour indabas (affairs and disputes) in the shortest and most appropriate way possible – by mouth, failing that with his fists or, in difficult cases, with a pick handle. The plaintive tone of his voice never seemed to change or waver, whether the news was good or (more usually) bad, or (sometimes) an improbable series of catastrophes. His wife enjoyed the monopoly of making beer in camp. As with many publicans, a good share of the profits was drunk by Njara, usually at weekends, occasionally (and against orders) during the week, the excuse being unforeseen rapid fermentation.

The previous week, some hideous screaming from the camp had obliged me to intervene in a vicious drunken fight between Njara and Mangasai. The latter, with great presence of mind when he saw me coming, stopped defending himself and shouted out, "I cannot beat my bossboy." After he had endured several more blows I managed to haul him away from Njara and patch him up.

Though never having bothered with a blasting licence, Njara was excellent and safe with explosives. It was a reassuring sight to see Njara strolling along holding his carefully trimmed priming stick, his deep trouser pockets bulging with sticks of dynamite, detonators carefully wrapped and padded in his breast pocket, and white fuse wire coiled over his shoulder like climbing rope. If at times consumption of explosives was a little heavy, this was compensated for by the choice bream that appeared on our table, and for which we readily perjured ourselves to a suspicious fisheries officer. The dregs of the beer would be thrown into a corner of the lake to attract fish which were then stunned by the dynamite and collected from the surface where they floated. Although thus falling short of perfection in some respects, on balance Njara was an excellent chap to have around on your side and I didn't want to lose him.

Thus it was that I found myself going to try and bail him out of jail. Njara, "the hungry one", had apparently given further proof of his prowess by beating up several native policemen in the municipal beer hall. According to eye-witness accounts which had even reached the local newspaper, it had been spectacularly well done. I had somehow felt it might have been a mistake to leave some of my gang in town for three nights while en route for the south.

I had to go to the familiar police station at the end of Cairo Road adjacent to the native township. There I found an unrepentant and complaining Njara sharing a small cell with five others. After cautioning him to keep his mouth shut in court, look straight at the magistrate, and answer briefly and respectfully when essential, I tackled the clerk. After consultations with a rather hostile police inspector, who said it was a serious matter, it was finally agreed that Njara's case could come up late the following morning. I happened to know the magistrate who enjoyed a hand of bridge. By good fortune I was invited to make up a four that evening, and took care to be on my best behaviour, choosing an appropriate moment to compliment him on his good play.

Case loads in the town court were always heavy and many would come to watch the proceedings with interest. There was a startled gasp from the crowded courtroom as three bandaged, sheepish, and sullen native policemen took their seats near the witness box, followed by Njara with the deceptive look of wide-eyed injured innocence that I knew so well. A newly appointed African police lieutenant indignantly summarised the evidence. Clearly, the police had it in for Njara, who apparently had previous convictions for fighting, drunkenness, and disorderly conduct. On this occasion, he had apparently become fighting drunk, threatened people with a knife and a broken beer bottle, and then insulted and assaulted the police who had been sent to restore order.

Njara began quietly enough. Yes, he had bought one beer, but had not even begun to drink it, and was certainly not drunk. Other people were fighting and he was only attempting to stop them. The police, when they arrived, attacked him, Njara, for no reason whatsoever. It was possible that he may have put his hand up to protect himself and one of the policemen may have touched it. He had however never seen these three policemen before in his life. He had certainly never suggested that they were a bunch of sexually inadequate syphilitic perverts, although – Njara was warming up – everyone knew it was true of their tribe. I tried to catch his eye. Given an audience, Njara was inclined to be unpredictable. Mercifully, he shut up.

I was given leave to speak as his employer. Njara's conduct as a highly respected and senior workman was impeccable. He was never known to be drunk and detested physical violence. It was possible that he may have erred in his younger days, but if so he was a changed character now. In any event, it seemed improper for the police to allege a police record against the accused before judgement (I was lucky on that one). Clearly, there must have been other people fighting the police to inflict all their injuries. Why were they not in court? How could one man possibly do all that damage to three well-trained police officers armed with truncheons? (I could have answered that rhetorical question very well, having seen Njara in action). Njara's future behaviour would be vouched for by me, etc.

Amidst incredulous scowls from all the police present, the bench, after speaking of "conflict of evidence" and "lack of independent corroboration of identity" found Njara guilty of only the lesser charge of disorderly behaviour and fined him ten shillings, which I paid on the spot.

As Njara and myself and the men, who had been enthralled spectators in the courtroom, were leaving, a furious senior inspector confronted me. "Any more lying from you and you will be on a charge yourself. Get these bastards out of town today." So we left. We were going anyway.

Somehow, I felt the pattern of my life was beginning to get a bit rough at the edges, indeed a bit pointless. I began to ask myself, not for the first time, what was I doing?!

Many months later, we had completed our work on part of the Great Dyke of Southern Rhodesia, some 300 miles long, the largest body of igneous rock in the world. We had proved the existence of a seam of metallurgical-grade chromite (the best kind, essential for the manufacture of stainless steel) where its existence had not been suspected before. The seam was admittedly patchy and more suitable to small-scale working than by a large company. Nevertheless, it could have been worked at a profit. Following a decision by head office, however, we filled in our trial workings and eventually packed up and left. I took Njara and one or two others with me, but I was obliged to leave behind a small work-force of men, some of them with families, who had built kayas and now had no work and no prospect of work in the area. Many had left their native villages and had no land either.

Looking at them as I left, the word "proletariat" took on added meaning for me. In fact, the vision of their faces as I drove away haunts me to this day. Some years later I was to profit professionally by writing three scientific papers based on this work.

* * * * * * *

Ben and Nine

Ben was a rascal, lazy and unrepentant, with no sense of honour or responsibility. During the eighteen months that he worked for me I never ceased to admire him. Looking back, it is clear to me now that Ben acted as a kind of safety valve in my relationship with the men. I admit that in the daily rough and tumble of itinerant camp life this essential function may at times have been overlooked!

His loneliness was the key to his behaviour. I never saw him meet a kinsman, and rarely heard him speak of his little known and small tribe whose home was several hundred miles away. We always reckoned there was a bit of the Bushman in Ben. His appearance, short, slight, and wiry with a complexion containing a hint of yellow in an overall light brown, was distinct from the local Bantu and immediately set him apart from his fellow workmen. I think he always thought he was being got at, and as far as work was concerned he was agin it. On safari he always managed to secure a small load, but despite this he would lag and arrive late at resting places, picking his way daintily with his tiny feet. The laughter of his comrades would so gall him that often he would not stop to rest with the others but proceed onwards in the van muttering to himself.

Our work, although generally interesting and tolerable, would often not be easy. Such tribulations as heat, distance, shortage of water and meat, bad weather, thick bush, long grass with ticks, getting lost, uncomfortable proximity to elephant, etc., were commonplace. The combinations were infinite. I can remember sometimes falling asleep with the sole consoling thought that tomorrow could not possibly be as bad as the day had been. Sometimes, it was worse! The first to complain on such occasions was, inevitably, Ben.

His complaining took the form of an incessant rapid jabbering, at times incomprehensible even to the men, in the form of parables on our probable fate. "Ben, shut up," would have been a commonly overheard remark by an observer. If asked to explain himself, Ben would step forward and with chimpanzee-like gestures with his hands and face, enlarge on the current theme for several minutes in Chilapalapa. When thus challenged, his complaints were generally so patently exaggerated and absurd that they aroused the derision of the men. Finally, overcome by their laughter, Ben would peter out, spit, and turn away. Notwithstanding this performance, many small grievances, or more accurately grievances that, if not acknowledged, might have assumed genuine proportions later, were brought to my notice in this way and crises averted.

Njara, the headman whose business it should have been to tactfully attempt the same task, seldom bothered about little things until they had assumed serious proportions. I always thought Njara got a fatalistic kind of satisfaction in presenting, usually at dawn, some insoluble difficulty or problem over a foreseeable detail!

Ben was undoubtedly intelligent and he was also very knowledgeable indeed in the ways of animals – they often figured in his "parables". It was a great pity that he had not the slightest sense of responsibility (at least as it appeared to me). Any job left in his hands would be shoddily done. Ben was capable of good work but, as I have mentioned, he was agin it.

Ben's domestic affairs were a bit of a trial to him. I shouldn't have been surprised to learn that he was on the run. He certainly added to any difficulties he may have had by acquiring a young girl of a rather forward disposition who was herself on the run from her husband. The latter was pursuing Ben for twenty-five Pounds compensation in the local traditional court, but said Ben could keep the girl. Ben was paying this in instalments but at the same time was intending to appeal in the European magistrate's court (the proper charge was fifteen Pounds, but Ben had been unfairly treated because he was alien), when the girl ran away from him stealing some of his few possessions. Ben maintained that he was eligible for restitution over and above his remaining debt to the former husband and this too was to go to court. I never knew what the outcome was, because we moved permanently to another area taking Ben with us, but I think he was relieved to accompany us.

Perhaps I retained special ties with Ben and put up with him because, and I am ashamed to say this, he was the first native, indeed the only native, whom I ever struck in anger, actually more in frustration, although that is no excuse.

It all happened on a rather difficult mission undertaken in the height of the rains. Njara and Pedro (my cook) were in jail. Njara merited it. Pedro was, I suspected, a more or less an innocent bystander in the incident that got them both arrested. Anyway, we were without the services of two key men. The assignment I had, along with Glen, was an unusual one. I had taken instructions from Lusaka over the phone in a tin hut on the line of rail, and I couldn't hear properly because of the noise of rain on the tin roof. The assignment was to locate and sample amethyst deposits in the area downstream from the Victoria Falls on the north side of the Zambezi. We were to bring back a cubic yard of amethyst. I learnt later that what the boss had really meant was how much amethyst was there per cubic yard – not, incidentally, a valid way of evaluating the type of deposit in which the amethyst occurred. Also, typical of the company, we were not given any reference to the excellent work of a former government geologist who had discovered and described the deposits many years previously. Since then, no one had visited them, so we were very much on our own and in the dark.

We did, however, at this time enjoy the luxury of two short-wheelbase land-rovers, although both were in a clapped-out condition. We had to fill them up, plus extra petrol in four-gallon cans, at the Indian store in Pemba. We didn't have enough cash on us, so we decided to fill up first before asking for credit. The Indian then started protesting as well he might – senior members of the African Congress had similarly been demanding petrol from him (the difference being that we came back to pay). With great presence of mind his wailing protests changed to a faint "I trust you" as we receded into the distance!

We drove the land-rovers to the nearest access point, Kalomo Mission station, over a pretty poor track. All fords were flooded. At one, a particularly steep one which also appeared to be deep, I had stopped and was preparing to check its depth and reconnoitre for boulders under the water and possibly disconnect the fan belt, when Glen charged past me in his land rover and took the ford at a gallop. Not to be outdone, I followed and after a wet and very bumpy passage came to a halt beside him on the brim on the far side. Glen looked rather pale – his brakes had failed, thus accounting for his macho approach to the ford!

Enough of land rovers. We had to continue on foot along an old trail known as Walker's Drift trail. This wound down through hilly escarpment country to a place where in the pioneer days the Zambezi had been fordable by ox-wagon in the dry season – an area of sandy flats where the Zambezi emerges from the gorges some sixty miles below the Falls. This old trail was now in an atrocious condition, overgrown, badly churned up by the passage of elephant, and in places difficult to follow at all. Usefully, however, its route provided access to several small rivers, where we located float of amethyst.

There was one place I remember well. It was on the edge of a small clearing and I had paused to see where to go. Suddenly I received a hearty shove in the small of the back and staggered forward three or four paces very nearly on top of a large green python lying asleep in a coil in the grass. It slithered off harmlessly. I was not amused. The man who had pushed me was someone I had always liked, Nine. Nine pointed up to where I had been standing before being unceremoniously shoved. Still there on a branch at head height was a narrow tree-snake with its red tongue flickering. It's native name translates as "if he bites you, you will live just long enough to see the smoke of your kaya, then die". The snake had apparently been preparing to strike me. The presence of the python, unseen by either of us beforehand, was just a coincidence! We managed a good laugh over that one.

The distance was considerable and progress much more arduous than we had anticipated. In a night bivouac we could hear some drumming, presumably from a village not very far away. No one knew of any village in this difficult country and some of the men appeared apprehensive. Next morning, we found that some men had apparently deserted, among them to my great surprise Nine, the man whose alertness had quite possibly saved my life the previous day, and whom to my lasting regret I never saw again. He was a quiet mature man who often took it upon himself to lead in difficult places and had always, as on the previous afternoon, looked after me. I never understood why he left.

We were all a bit damp, cold, and hungry, and reduced numbers made for harder work all round. It was later that day, when Ben started up in a way that looked like disturbing the remaining men, that I lost my temper, pushed him up against a tree and thumped him. I apologised to him afterwards. He could not be said to have accepted my apology, just grinned to himself and turned away. He knew and I knew that I had broken my own unspoken code of behaviour. Moreover, I had been cowardly in picking on him, the smallest man.

We prospected by tracing stream float and located amethyst veins in some low cliffs of basalt. The amethyst was quite impressive. It occurred in clumps of large six-sided prismatic crystals with pyramid terminations and with zones of colour. The base of each clump of crystals was greenish, then milky white, and then milky purple. Here and there, the very tips of some crystals, where they projected into cavities in the dark basalt, were formed of the more highly prized transparent purple amethyst.

We came across several other similar localities, and we were sure that there would be more. On the face of it, however, they were not the sort of mineral deposits likely to attract the interest of a large company, because they were dispersed and individually small. They would be far more suitable for "tributers" (prospectors working for themselves and paying some percentage to the company holding the concession), or even for native prospectors working the area for themselves.

A cubic yard was out of the question, but we loaded up with sacks of the amethyst, plodded back to the land-rovers, and eventually deposited the amethyst in Chartered Exploration's store in Lusaka a few days later. It was quite a sight. The government survey geologists came over to look.

Nothing further was done at the time. Many years later, I chanced to look at some yearly handbook about Zambia. It mentioned mining production, mainly, of course, copper, but included amethyst exports worth nearly one million Pounds! On reading this, the first recollections to come to my mind were my memories of Ben and Nine.

* * * * * * *

Gold at Lungu Hill

The company, for once, had shown some imagination in pairing me off with an old prospector for a visit to reputed gold showings occurring near Lungu Hill in the far north of Northern Rhodesia. It was to prove a happy and productive partnership. Moreover, on this occasion, there was an unusual added note of poignancy. My partner, Walter, had in his possession a crude plan showing sites of alleged rich gold pannings in the area which he had been given by one of his cronies who had now passed away. One could say that we found "gold" all right, though not quite the variety we had sought.

Fate usually treated the pioneer prospectors pretty badly. Very few of them ever struck it rich, despite a lot of hard work and hardship in the bush. Even when they did, they were generally not well rewarded, and were often exploited by the large mining companies. I guess Walter was glad to be on a payroll for a while, although he always spoke with nostalgia of the times when he was prospecting solo, and particularly of the time he worked two small gold claims that he had discovered, the *Iron Hat* and the *Flowing Bowl*, the only time he had ever had money in his pocket. He had recently come up from Southern Rhodesia whence he and his brother had to flit following annoying police investigations into their gold mine near Que Que. Their "gold mine" was in fact a front operation for marketing gold purloined by native miners from the *Globe and Phoenix* mine, where the gold is often richly visible in the stopes.

So, we were on our way to Bemba country close to where the Congo [Zaire], Tanganyika [Tanzania], and Northern Rhodesia [Zambia] meet near the southern end of Lake Tanganyika. We drove two land rovers in convoy for three days with all our equipment on dirt roads over the endless flat plateau country of Central Africa. Here and there the monotony was broken by an odd range or hill, which would obviously have had significance as landmarks over the ages. We had digressed at one point to where a river unexpectedly cascades over a lip of contorted quartzite outcrops to produce the seldom-visited Kundalila Falls ("falls of the singing dove"). They were surprisingly high, delicate and beautiful.

On our eventual arrival, we paid a courtesy visit to the office of the District Commissioner in Kasama, to whom we had previously sent the customary letter about our intentions. He proved, fairly predictably, to be a middle-aged, middle-class, medium-brained Englishman. "But you can't go there. I can't allow it. It's not safe. It's a hotbed of Congress [the newly formed African National Congress party aiming for self-government]. They're giving us a lot of trouble just now. Besides, they're planning to receive you with a food and labour boycott."

But how did they know we were coming unless someone in his office who had seen our letter had prematurely told them, we asked. He looked around at his bright African cadet, his industrious clerks (guilty to a man of petty corruption), and his uniformed messengers (overfed, fat, and lazy to a man) – his world. Our logic was unanswerable. He made the only possible reply: bluster. "I find your remarks very insulting." So we said goodbye. Under the law of the Territory, he couldn't stop us going prospecting and he knew it.

In the end, he delegated his District Officer, a Scot, to come with us. "Aye, you've come at a bad time, but we'll see what we can do. Our people here are very upset about the old charter freeholds being taken up and fenced by companies for ranching. They never knew the land wasn't legally theirs although their chiefs had been told." This smacked of a deal being made with the chiefs alone for some consideration involving land which was not theirs anyway but their people's – a fairly typical colonial manoeuvre. We got the feeling, though nothing was said explicitly, that the D.O.'s opinion of his boss was not dissimilar to our own.

The D.O. was as good as his word. He spoke on our behalf to a convened gathering of local chiefs, headmen, and local authority secretaries. They received all he had to say in silence and departed. So there we were without the labour that usually comes flocking to a new camp. We walked around a bit, found what might have been the old prospector's campsite, and visited a few villages where we were unable to buy any chickens, eggs, or vegetables.

It was beginning to look as if we would have to get labour in from elsewhere. The outlook was not pleasant. Then one morning two characters presented themselves at our camp, dressed in white overalls, trousers, socks, and shiny black shoes. "We would like work, please." "Man, this place gets crazier each day. Look here, our work is dirty, walking through the bush, and working with picks and shovels." "That's all right, bwana, we like it." "The pay is one shilling and a penny a day plus sixpence skoff money." They shrugged their shoulders and accepted.

We took them on with some apprehension and started prospecting. After two or three days, the taller of the two, a quiet, good-looking young man, very intelligent and with excellent English surprised us. "Well, we see that you are not after our land, you are truly prospecting; if we find anything, there will be work here for our men instead of them having to live away from home in the Copper-Belt. Tomorrow there will be more men for work."

Next morning shortly after dawn James and the smaller of the two, John Biscott, more excitable, whose small frame disguised amazing vitality, were organising and presenting some fifteen or so men. "This man is very strong and would be useful for digging; this man knows the country well because he is a hunter," etc.

Thus it came about that we worked in the Lungu district with the local African National Congress secretary and treasurer, by now more appropriately clothed and shod, as our newly appointed headmen!! Labour troubles of any kind were immediately and reasonably settled. Food became plentiful. The D.C. was infuriated as it came to his ears that James and John when on safari with us visited villages on Congress business. This rather tickled us.

On one weekend we took James and John with us to visit the fabulous Kalambo Falls, a reputed nine hundred feet high, and even more remote than Kundalila. The water of the river, one of the sources of the Congo, comes over a vertical cliff in one great spout that mostly dissolves into mist before reaching the gorge below. The gorge goes on to drop a total of three thousand feet in the five miles from the plateau to the southern tip of Lake Tanganyika. I have a stunning photograph of the gorge spanned by a double rainbow in the misty spray below the falls, on the lip of which I had been standing. The cliff is one of the rare nesting sites of malibou storks which silently glided around on air currents above the gorge. We also used to go and have a party on the lake steamer when she docked every two weeks at Mpulungu, the southern terminus of her run on Lake Tanganyika. So we had quite a good time.

We even found some gold, too. At least we confirmed some stream pannings, but they were very localised and the strata from which they were coming were too low a grade to work. A scintillometer survey indicated that there were only very low uranium values as well. So the company's dream of a second Rand was a chimera!

Eventually then our reconnaissance work was completed. I like to think the moral of this little tale was something said by my partner, a man incidentally of very few words (a virtue seldom found in man, even more rarely in woman) after a couple of incidents during the work. One day I had borrowed his short-wheelbase landrover to get to a place along a route which we intended to make into a road and had lurched twice against trees damaging the bodywork somewhat. "My God," he said, when I got back rather late, "Look at that." Over dinner, I noticed my long-wheelbase wasn't around. "Oh, its in a water hole. Didn't see it in time. Bit bent.

James is borrowing some oxen and tackle to pull it out." Next day, James retrieved my landrover and, using only a large and a small hammer, and working until sunset, did a first-class job of panel beating on both vehicles.

Some time later I was way out in the bundu with John and some men. We were having to cut some thickety undergrowth in one or two places in order to get through some overgrown steep and rocky country when one man sliced his leg with a panga. To see Africans working barefoot and barelegged with these heavy-bladed all-purpose forest knives cum hatchets, not dissimilar to a butcher's cleaver, is to wonder why accidents such as these are so few. When they do happen, they were frequently bad as now. Blood was coming in spurts and we had a desperate job temporarily arresting it. We felt we needed to get him into medical care, but how? John volunteered to go with one of the men direct over several wild miles of hills and precipices and bring the land-rover round to the nearest accessible point to where we were. They must have gone like the wind because no sooner had we carried the injured man the two miles or so to our agreed meeting point they were there with the vehicle. The man recovered OK.

"Well," Walter said over his pipe that evening, "There's only one thing wrong with those two beggars." "What's that?" I asked, defensively. "That there's not another ten thousand like them in this blasted territory," came the unexpected reply.

But the winds of change were to affect us all, sooner than we ever could have envisaged.

* * * * * * *

The Dawn

I was in camp high up on the Nyanga plateau in Nyasaland [Malawi]with distant views of Lake Nyasa itself. Livingstone had been here nearly a century before and, so the apocryphal story goes, on sighting the waters of the great lake, asked what it was called, and had received the obvious answer: "nyasa" (= lake). So, allegedly, he christened it with the pleonasm Lake Nyasa!

Summer rains had broken as usual, but this year was different to any I had ever experienced before. True, the tension built up in the hot end to the long dry season had finally been resolved, after the usual several false starts and summer lightning barren of rain, by copious and cooling rains. But there was another tension in the air that had to do with the people themselves.

I had been aware that virtually for the first time in Africa, I had suddenly been unable to obtain provisions from the villages nearby. The old man from Chikuni's village, the nearest, who had always been pleased to drop by with a bottle of milk and stay for a chat had stopped coming. And no longer did young girls with laughing eyes come with fruit and eggs and stay to stare and giggle.

Another thing I had noticed was the cessation for some weeks of drumming and singing of any kind in the evenings. No songs of rejoicing and fertility as the green corn started to grow long in the ear. I had also observed some unusual comings and goings, noticeably of two or three "townie" Africans to the nearby villages. On one occasion, two of them had pointedly ignored my traditional greeting in Chinanga. In the field work, there had been a couple of inexplicable desertions and some lapses of concentration, the men concerned not forthcoming with the usual voluble explanations of varying degrees of credibility. My headman was uncharacteristically withdrawn.

It was if the whole country of Nyasaland, "the country of the lake" was tense. As powerful as the immutable rhythm of the seasons was a countrywide feeling of expectancy. But of what? Granted, there had been some political shenanigans to do with the newfangled "Federation" of Rhodesia and Nyasaland, a clumsy device intended to maintain white supremacy over an impracticably wide area. But this was Nyasaland, always sleepy and peaceful, practically devoid of white settlers, and always non-political.

The waters of the great lake rippled and laughed as they had always done. Silent and preoccupied, Nyasaland waited and watched in silence. Did I consciously question what might come to pass, or was I too carried along unresisting in a spell? Meanwhile, the pattern of life went on, with nothing untoward to a casual observer, in this lovely corner of Africa.

Then, one evening, it happened. I was first aware of the big talking drum in the village to the south beating out a short rhythmic message, repeated continually, corresponding to the speech pattern of some well-understood phrase. Now that I was listening intently, I could distinguish even more distant drums from further south that might have been beating before. Suddenly, the same message was taken up by Chikuni's village. In my mind's eye, I could visualise the drummer, whom I knew, transmitting his message surrounded by many of the villagers and children. Then in intervals between the nearer noise I could distinguish the same message from first one, then two, villages further north, urgently answering and confirming. The night air was alive with the big drums, such as I had never known it before. Later, the rhythm of the talking drums changed and became faster, and eventually they ceased and their place was taken by the more common village drums, making up for the silence of the previous weeks. Swifter than the flight of any bird, the message reached every corner of the country of the lake that night.

A group of figures, men, women, and children, filed slowly by the light of two hurricane lamps into my camp site. They came singing that beautiful song *Nkosi sikalele Africa*, God bless Africa. They formed a semi-circle around me, singing first in unison, then singing naturally and powerfully in harmonious part song, the men echoing the women's cry, Nkosi sikalele Africa, hauntingly plaintive rather than militant. My headman stepped forward and addressed me quietly. He explained that tomorrow would be a holiday, and maybe for two days after as well, as the beer would not be ready until then as they had not been making it recently. I would not be able to leave my camp because the road down the escarpment was blocked by fallen trees. He and two others would sleep outside my tent to protect me. In the nicest possible way, I suppose I was being told I was a prisoner!

My "imprisonment" did not prevent me from walking over to Chikuni's village a couple of days later. I found Chikuni and a few elders seated under a shade tree. As I approached them, one of the elders spoke up and informed me that freedom had come, the dawn, "kwacha", for which everyone had been waiting and preparing. By great good luck, some women already had got beer ready, and I was invited to partake. The strained atmosphere of the previous weeks dissolved. Smiles everywhere took the place of sullen looks. Gifts of milk and honey, a chicken and some eggs were offered to me.

This, incidentally, was an emergency, during which the call came through on the radio for all whites to report to government bomas for their own protection and all able-bodied men to report for emergency militia duty. I decided that such heroics were not for me. I felt quite safe where I was, anyway! I'm afraid, however, that some, like my friend Monnie, had very different stories to tell.

* * * * * * *

Monnie's Story

We are told that many men of great strength are to be found among the gentlest. My friend Monnie was such a one. Very quiet, tall and powerful, though not what one would call handsome, he was like a significant minority of Afrikaaners in having dark hair and appealing big brown eyes – quite likely a touch of the tar brush. He spoke English in a soft attractive accent, very dissimilar to the customary harsh tones of a Boer speaking an alien tongue he doesn't like. His workmates used to rag him a little and take advantage of him, and his sharp little wife led him a bit of a dance.

Everyone agreed that all he needed to do to cure her was to administer one gentle beating. However, I do not believe Monnie had ever even dreamed of laying a finger on anyone in anger, white people that is. With the Kaffirs I'm afraid it was different. In speaking to them he would at times assume the persona of the Boer, based on baaskop, albeit tempered with a good deal of understanding of the ragged bunch of labourers that worked in the Salisbury station yard. Once, during a dispute, he laid three of them out with a pick handle and frequently used to handle them roughly. On the other hand, I once saw him share his last cigarettes with two Africans.

Funnily enough, with an intuitive understanding of a person's true nature, the labourers liked and respected him, and worked better for him than for many of the other white men. Their first nickname for him, "he who blinks" (Monnie had a barely perceptible tic) was in process of being replaced by the honoured one of "big elephant" by virtue of his strength and passivity, sometimes broken by sudden temper.

Their respect was not shared by one black man, a clerk who worked in the office with Monnie. This man, unexpectedly promoted on account of a recent government concession to the pace of advancement of African railway workers, was better educated than Monnie, better at figures, and annoyingly good at remembering the odd little details of goods-yard forwarding procedure that Monnie sometimes overlooked. Monnie hated him, treated him worse than any of the others, but prudently didn't touch him. One occasion when his tic only really became noticeable was when they had to consult.

Monnie's chief weekend relaxation was hunting. In part he did it to get away from his wife. Working at this time in Southern Rhodesia (which I didn't like), I found myself in Salisbury (which I detested) on occasional weekends, so I too was glad to get away.

Monnie and I used to camp out some Saturday nights and shoot in the evening, sometimes (illegally) at night, and also at dawn as well. Monnie was an excellent shot, far excelling myself. With typical generosity he would often leave easier targets for me. I learnt a lot from him and some of the best times I ever had were spent camping rough with Monnie and doing everything for ourselves. Often we found ourselves in the places which the little Bushmen had used long ago and where they had painted the overhanging rock of a granite kopje with records of their hunting successes and their totem dances, and had protected themselves against evil spirits by painting the sign of the crossed hands. At one place, I was convinced that the Bushman artist who had painted some totem dancers must have been the same artist who had painted similar figures at a place I had discovered well over a hundred miles away near the Mvuradonas. In such places, we would sit and cook and smoke and silently look over the bush country and cleared tobacco lands. There is something very satisfying about hunting which obviously goes back to our pre-agricultural psyches.

I was therefore somewhat at a loss when Monnie was called up for emergency duty that year. Before he left Salisbury I saw him once on sentry duty outside the barracks. Our brief conversation was terminated by the arrival of officers who looked rather meaningly at Monnie and myself and the near ring of native children at the gate watching with wondering eyes the army (all white) at work. Then, suddenly, he was gone, airlifted to Nyasaland. News, some of it not very pleasant, a plenty in the newspapers but private news from Monnie none, although I recall dropping a line to him twice.

I didn't know he was back in town until I saw him one day in surprising circumstances. While I was driving along in a steady stream of traffic along one of Salisbury's main streets I saw a heavily laden native woman with several children waiting to cross. She was carrying one child on her back and on her head was a large cardboard box tied up with strips of bark. Her appearance and manner suggested that she was unused to this ugly city. Suddenly a white man stepped from the pavement, took the two children by the hand, and shepherded the whole family across the busy street under the wondering stares of pedestrians. It was Monnie. You will understand Salisbury a little better if I were to explain that such behaviour was incredible and unbelievable for a white man. By the time I had stopped and got back to the place, Monnie was gone.

I found him next day at work, very quiet as was usual with him. "I saw you yesterday." "Oh, where?" "In Abercorn Street helping that umfazi." Monnie looked at me quickly and blushed. He blushed very easily, I remember. "When are we going hunting, yon?" he asked. "OK," I replied. Nevertheless, it was not until several weeks later that we found ourselves over one of our evening campfires, and Monnie haltingly told me his story.

He had been flown to low-veldt country in Nyasaland, thinly administered, and badly so in Monnie's opinion, by a few English gentlemen types, "not like you" he had added, somewhat unnecessarily. They had panicked in the face of a peaceful but massive civil disobedience movement and had called in the army. The army's difficult job had been to round up and imprison those who appeared to be leaders, with the help of scanty and probably inaccurate security information. Much of their work was done at night in the early hours of the morning. On one such occasion, they had surrounded a village and on moving in had found many people at a meeting from which several had fled away in the moonlight. Obeying orders (a phrase I seemed to have heard somewhere before), Monnie fired and one of the fleeing figures fell. It was a woman and Monnie had been present when she died an hour later painfully and consciously, her eyes open but unspeaking, with terrible bleeding wounds in her breast and back.

Incidents such as these had hardened and dehumanised some of the young soldiers, but Monnie's burden had been insupportable. Wherever he went, he felt people looking at him as if they knew, and in one village the following incident occurred. Some villagers had come up to them with small gifts of food. Their spokesman explained that they knew he was the killer of the woman, they were sorry for him, and that was why they wanted to give him these small things. Whatever happened, they knew that freedom would be theirs shortly, and they bore no personal hostility towards any white man. Monnie's eyes became moist as he told me all this, and I can imagine the same had happened in the village. Some children had instinctively held his hand and Monnie had apparently broken down.

The scene had been witnessed by an officer and Monnie had been tried, found guilty, imprisoned, and discharged with ignominy for grave breaches of discipline (he had apparently been insolent to an officer, as well). I have to say that Monnie's actual remarks to me revealed more common sense than any to be found in the whole of government: "Those Kaffirs, man, they knew, I tell you, they knew I killed her. That country, man, it's beautiful, but it's Kaffir country, it's theirs, why not let them have it."

I suppose it would be pleasant to record that Monnie became a changed man devoting his spare time to good works, promoting interracial harmony, etc., but some time after I left, I heard that such was not the case. Monnie lost his touch with the labourers, his tic became worse, he was in court for striking the clerk, his wife was separated from him (no great loss), he lost his job, and his army record was held against him when he tried to find other work.

God knows what happened to Monnie, but I wish him well, amidst all the personal debris of a continent that seemed to be undergoing physical and social disintegration.

* * * * * * *

The young D.A.

District Assistant Rennington was the first administrative officer to spend a whole rainy season down in the Zambezi rift valley. Two missionaries spent their lives there, but their quarters, in contrast to Rennington's camp, were stone-built and relatively comfortable. Rennington, whom I had met briefly in Choma, a tall fresh-cheeked youth of about twenty-five years of age, had been despatched to the valley on a matter of some importance and urgency.

I encountered him again on his return with numerous porters up to the plateau. He had camped for the night not far away from me, and came over to see me. I was startled at his appearance. His eyes were staring and he seemed to be in a state of shock. This is the story he told me over a meal.

His task had appeared straightforward enough. The previous dry season, surveyors had staked out the level to which the waters of the new Lake Kariba, some two hundred miles long, would eventually rise when the great new dam was complete. Rennington's job was to explain this in good time to the chiefs, headmen, and villagers of the Valley Tonga, many of whom would perforce have to be moved to new sites.

It should perhaps be remarked that the valley people tended to regard the white man with indulgent respect born out of genuine amusement and appreciation of his entertainment value. They had no money and did not need it. Consequently, they did not take readily to the notion of working for it. Because of their "backwardness", they were excused from paying the otherwise ubiquitous native poll-tax of seven shillings and sixpence per year. This tax, incidentally, was cajoled and extorted from all male adults on routine annual visits to villages by the D.A.s. (The answer was simple: the men would leave the village and come back after the D.A. had moved on, after listening to endless tales from the women of the wholesale death and desertion of husbands.) The colonial administration did not provide roads or primary schools in the valley, did not nag village headmen to have latrines dug, did not instruct them in alien forms of local government, and did not bother the people with police. In short, the valley people were deprived of many of the benefits of civilisation and managed to remain remarkably content without them.

Rennington's first move, although entirely logical, proved to be a great mistake. He pitched his camp close to Sinazongwe, the village of the Paramount Chief. The Chief's very name, Siamenda, "father of waters", seemed to be a propitious omen of success for his mission. The Chief's authority would then greatly help in the education of all the other chiefs and headmen. Furthermore, the network of native paths radiating from Sinazongwe also made it the logical centre for his work.

Paramount Chief Siamenda immediately conceived an enduring liking for the young white man. To the horror of some of his elders, Siamenda, eschewing the conventional retinue of attendants, would personally visit

Rennington's camp, bringing with him presents of chickens, eggs, occasionally a goat or a young pig. Of course, he expected to receive some presents in exchange! Rennington's previous conscientious practice of the vernacular enabled him to converse with the Chief with some facility. In short, they got on famously. When Siamenda learnt of Rennington's desire to stay for several months, he brought with him on his next visit a beautiful young girl of about sixteen. Her comely appearance was increased by a hair-do of red mud, her nose elegantly pierced by a bone, her body well-greased. Siamenda was disappointed and a little perplexed when Rennington hurriedly refused this offer of someone to keep him company during his stay in the valley, but did not let the incident influence his friendship for the young man.

Siamenda could not have been more helpful when Rennington told him of the purpose of his visit and the meaning of the survey. Siamenda explained that the surveyors' pegs did not go straight and had appeared to make considerable diversions in order to save going more directly over quite small hills. Consequently, he had given orders for better routes to be selected in places where the white men had obviously got a little disorientated. The wooden stakes had not been difficult to move. Indeed, some villagers had been collecting the ones with interesting markings, partly out of curiosity. Siamenda had intervened to try and stop this practice, but it was difficult to stop it completely as the stakes were believed to be powerful magic. The occasional concrete pillars had presented more difficulty and most of these had been left even where obviously out of place, but now that the rains were making the ground softer, the positions of some of these too were now being rectified.

With growing apprehension, Rennington attempted to explain the true purpose of the survey in some detail. He produced a plan of the valley and the proposed new lake. This was much admired by Siamenda who brought his elders along to see it. They did not quite understand what it meant, but a youth who had learnt to read in a mission school on the plateau showed them Sinazongwe written on the map. This gave everyone considerable pleasure, and the spot soon came to be identified by a greasy superposition of fingerprints. Rennington talked, of course, of the great dam to be built far away downstream at the place called Kariba. This was so far away that no one had ever visited it, although several old men recollected that an enormous snake was reputed to live in the river there, and in fact could be sighted some years at the season of low water. Rennington talked of electricity, of electric light, and railways, and mines. Yes, Siamenda said, they knew or had heard of most of these things: paraffin lamps, the sitema on which the white men sweated to throw black rocks on the fire, the mines, yes, where they cut trees to make big fires for the machines. The young white man was really quite knowledgeable and it was a pleasure to have him around.

In desperation, one day Rennington arranged to take Siamenda and a group of his people a walk to where some of the surveyors' marks had been left in position. This, said Rennington, is where the waters of the Zambezi will rise in four year's time. Siamenda was greatly interested and held a rapid consultation with his elders. At its end he said "Tomorrow, come with us. We have something to show you." The next day, Siamenda, late middle-aged, grey flecks appearing in his still thick curly black hair, a little overweight but very strong, immensely enjoyed the eight-mile stroll through part of his domain in the greenhouse-like atmosphere. He allowed himself to be carried on a litter a substantial part of the way. Then followed another consultation with his elders. Siamenda turned to Rennington. His friend, the young white man, had been interested in the water of the Zambezi. Well, here was the place where, some sixty years ago, the waters had reached during a uniquely high annual flood of the river. And that flood, old people had said at the time, was the highest ever known. Since that time, no other annual high water had risen nearly so high. The white men would be quite safe from any possible danger of flooding where they had put their posts and stakes and had no need to worry at all.

Rennington, somewhat affected by the heat and exertion, had insisted on his explanation and had become a little excited, even a bit hysterical. With tender solicitude, Siamenda insisted that the young white man be carried back to Sinazongwe and his camp. Clearly, the heat was temporarily affecting his young friend's brain. His nervousness about the rising of the Zambezi was clearly unjustified and illogical. A rest would put things right.

After a further week or so, Rennington came to realise that explanation was impossible. Further attempts were merely arousing doubts of his sanity among the people of Sinazongwe, who along with their Chief continued to visit him and ply him with gifts. Rennington sent a long letter to the District Commissioner. A messenger took it in a cleft stick and covered the long journey through the escarpment country and beyond at a steady lope of five miles an hour, and returned with a reply from the District Commissioner six days later.

Rennington showed me the letter. It went, I recall, something like this:

> Dear Rennington,
>
> Your note to hand. I am a little surprised at its tone, and I am replying personally as I feel that an official letter on file at this early stage in your career could be prejudicial to you.

You must realise that these people are not savages. I know Siamenda to be a fine old gentleman with perfect manners and a very good brain. You must exercise your imagination in explaining things to him. Time is very important -- that is why you are there at what I realise is a trying time of year. I am glad to hear that your health is good and, as you will see from your written instructions, I hope you will cover as much of the area as you can before next April, when I look forward to reading your final report.

I well remember my own early difficulties in Somalia – I think I may have spoken of them to you. That is why I am writing personally to ask you to pull yourself together and apply yourself single-mindedly to this important task. We all have to go through the mill.

Sincerely,
G.R.C. Braithwaite-Smyth

So, for five torrid months, Rennington had travelled the Valley, wearily explaining something that he knew would not be believed to wondering villagers. As a personal favour, Siamenda had kindly insisted on one or more of his own personal messengers accompanying Rennington on each of his safaris. The messengers were entrusted to ensure that Rennington was kindly received wherever he went, and to request that the white man's continuing anxiety about flooding was to be assuaged wherever possible by the recollections of local headmen on the behaviour of the river.

But, alas, tragedy was to take the place of farce.

* * * * * * *

Zambezi

Yes, farce became tragedy. The first thing was a very minor tragedy, still perhaps more in the realms of farce. The day after I had seen Rennington he came back to my camp. Again, he looked shaken. His camp had been burnt down, or more precisely, the grass fence around his camp had caught fire and his tent had gone up in flames as well. I should explain that it was the custom for travelling government staff to have their men build a circular grass fence around each and every campsite in order to provide privacy. It was all rather elaborate and fussy. Rennington was sure it was arson carried out by members of the African National Congress. It was one of their current bag of tricks in some other areas. Did I, he asked plaintively, think there might be any Congress around here?

I looked at him in amazement. It was common knowledge that Congress enjoyed very wide support throughout Northern Rhodesia by this time. I told him so. It was his turn to look amazed. So, I pointed to my cook who was just bringing us some tea. "He's Congress," I told Rennington. Pedro came along with the tea, making appropriate clucking noises. "You see my bossboy standing over there by the land-rover; he's Congress, too." Bonwero came over and expressed sympathy and pointed out that no one was against the D.A. himself. Congress would be the last to do him any harm. It was more a matter of making a protest, nothing personal. "You see the men over there; many of them are certainly Congress." They waved cheerfully at Rennington. "So you see, they're mostly all Congress and that goes for most of the villagers around here now." Rennington still looked a little stupefied.

The fact was that even during the relatively short time that Rennington had been isolated in the rift valley, Congress had massively increased its membership. I remember talking with the local Chief, Chona, around this time. He was very concerned that Congress were subverting the authority of the chiefs. In principle he was opposed to the Congress politicians, but in practice he had little choice but to go along with them. One of his sons was in fact to become a respected member of the first nationalist government quite shortly afterwards.

So, poor Rennington went back to the government boma and submitted his report. I saw him there some weeks later. He had recovered his health and good spirits. He was a decent chap, and I was glad to have a chat with him. Then, along came the D.C. What was I doing there wasting the time of his staff without his permission? I replied evenly that such visiting had always been customary in the area. I couldn't honestly say that I took to our Mr. Braithwaite-Smyth. The previous D.C. had been a much-respected man and had always had the time of day for callers. In fact, I had enjoyed his hospitality at dinner on more than one occasion. He understood his people well, travelled a lot in his district, much of it informally, and was well aware of the developing tensions. Because of his excellent work, he had been given promotion *with transfer* (the usual procedure in the Colonial Service), so he was no longer around at a critical time. But B-S (as we sometimes conveniently called him) was different. He sported a cane with some kind of embossed knob at the top, and flourished it rather like an officer's swagger-stick. He wore a neat cravat and impeccably clean and pressed khaki. When out in the bush, he gave orders that he was not to be disturbed by any visitors in the evenings and played classical music to himself on a portable gramophone.

Well, chacun a son goût. I have nothing against classical music. But I must say that one conversation I had with B-S alarmed me. Whereas Rennington's Paramount Chief Siamenda had been obtuse, I strongly suspected deliberately so, there was much more than obtuseness to worry about in the valley. Congress, irresponsibly, had been distributing membership cards there. The patter went something like this: "The white men are after your land in the valley. That is why they are planning to move you away from the river, where the good land is. What other reason could there be? If you pay ten shillings to join Congress, we will give you a card. When you produce this card, you will not have to leave your land." I mentioned the scale of this to B-S. His reply amazed me. "There is no Congress in the valley. I have forbidden it!"

And it was not, of course, just a question of losing pieces of arable land. For native animist people living in places inhabited by the spirits of their forefathers with many sacred trees and groves, burial grounds etc., to move permanently would be like cutting themselves off from their life and spirit. I honestly do not think that a serious appreciation of this ever occurred to some of the administration. Or perhaps, to be charitable, they were confronted with the unpleasant and inevitable task of eviction to make way for the waters of Lake Kariba and just realised they had to get on with it willy-nilly.

Not long after this, talks and negotiations with the Valley Tonga people seemed to have reached crisis point. But B-S had the answer, both imaginative and musical. He would send down the Territory's Askari band to play to them! So, the band was duly packed off in three lorries down the escarpment road from Gwembe, all the way to the Zambezi. I was not a witness to what happened, but I was told that the assembled villagers were hostile and frustrated and appeared menacing – although this I found difficult to imagine of the friendly and gentle Valley Tonga people that I had known. In any event, the members of the band were looking sideways at them while blowing away. Then some of them decided to stop playing and make for the lorries. The music apparently sputtered out and the concert ended in ignominious flight, with the members of the band just ahead of the triumphant villagers.

Well, it is very possible to win a battle but lose a war. Someone in government decided that the next foray into the Valley would not be with a band but with armed Askaris. Confrontation again ensued at the same place by the Zambezi. Again, I was not a witness as to how the events of the afternoon developed, but what finally transpired was a spear charge by the Valley Tonga men. They had consulted their shamans and had charms against injury. Liberally daubed with cow manure, they charged into the mouths of repeating rifles. The result was inevitable. In the year 1959, after this last spear charge in the glorious history of the British Empire, some nineteen native men lay dead and a substantial number were injured.

The Askaris suffered no losses. Later, I was to see some of the injured in the American mission hospital not far away. It was a pitiable sight to see wounds in humans, like those I was accustomed to seeing in hunted animals, which I would immediately dispatch and put out of their misery.

But we can't stand in the way of progress, can we?

* * * * * * *

Joli

Someone at head office in Johannesburg got the idea that we field geologists should acquire more experience of work underground, presumably so that we could see to what glorious ends our efforts in the field might lead if successful. So I spent some time on the Rand.

The very old chartered Dakota bumbled slowly southward on a course over the west side of the lake. Makeleni, along with about sixty others crammed into the little plane, peered out of the dirty windows between the cumulus clouds of summer at the beautiful country of the lake, their homeland. They knew that their families would look out for today's great silver bird bearing them to Joli, city of Gold, that white men call Johannesburg. The mines recruiting agent, known throughout all northern Nyasaland by his nickname roughly translatable as "finger-in-nose" on account of some unappealing personal habits, was in the plane with them on this occasion, reassuring them and joking fluently in the vernacular.

A generation ago, young men like these would have been painted white and taken to a remote and uninhabited part of the forest and left naked there to remain for a month, find food, hunt, shelter and protect themselves. Now they proved their manhood in Joli. Their wages were compulsorily saved and, by a sensible inter-government arrangement, transferred after their eighteen-month ordeal to a post-office account in Nyasaland. There it would provide such things as a bicycle, a saucepan radio, perhaps even a European suit, or be put towards the serious matter of bride price.

Makeleni had already acquired a wife, a pretty sloe-eyed girl from the next village whom he had known and liked all his life. He had been paying the bride price by instalments for two years – a most unsatisfactory procedure. At a word from her father, if the latter thought that payments were too slow or if he just felt he needed money, she would leave Makeleni without a word and return with their baby son to her father's house. This was despite the fact that she and Makeleni loved each other, that is to say they respected each other and behaved in all ways to each other as customs decreed, and never once doubted their rightness or their own happiness. Makeleni dreaded waking up and finding her gone, as had happened three times already. On these occasions he would have to go and see his father-in-law. Trying to cover his anger and distress with the necessary deep veneer of politeness and humility, he would endure the inevitable harangue culminating in a demand for money plus an extra gift of a goat for not, allegedly, paying on time. His agony would be all the more increased by the sight of his young wife with their baby on her back dutifully at work in her father's kaya and scarcely daring to look at him. Then he would desperately seek to borrow the necessary money, careless of the interest to be charged, in order to regain her.

Three weeks ago, he had told her of his decision to go to Joli. She had said, "Yes, it is good," and that was that. Privately they both deeply regretted his leaving, but bride price had increased several-fold in recent years. Though a living could be won from the land, actual cash (in lieu of the customary cattle) was scarce. So, without tears or visible emotion but with a lump in his throat, Makeleni had said goodbye to her.

The lust for gold had driven the white men to construct the deepest mines in the whole world at Joli. After a training period in which he had performed well enough, Makeleni learned that he was to work in Robinson Deep. Some of the others in the barrack quarters joked with him about it. You will not be cold there, they warned him.

So now each day Makeleni went down a vertical shaft a mile deep, then transferred to another cage for a further mile's descent, then walked for half an hour down a steep incline to reach his working place, twelve thousand feet below the surface. He was relatively lucky. Some men worked up to a further two thousand feet below. His score or so workmates on the shift were mainly Nyasalanders like himself, two from his own tribe. Their work was to lash the broken glassy rock, rich in invisible gold, from the narrow openings called stopes, where it had been drilled and broken by charges the previous shift, into two big shoe-like containers that shuttled interminably up and down the inclined shaft. Later in the shift, another small gang would already begin to drill with noisy hissing jack-hammers, while Makeleni's gang were still finishing lashing. Yet others constructed the large roof supports of cut logs arranged in criss-cross layers forming strong solid baulks of timber about four foot square that supported the roof of the stope which was about two and a half to three feet high. The pressure was so great that the rock flowed and squeezed these wooden baulks almost flat and closed the stope behind the advancing working face in about three weeks.

All this work was done under the direction of the shift boss, a white man called Render, strong, thick-necked, with huge hands who spoke gutturally to them in Chilapalapa and in a queer clipped English with the Mine Captain. Behind Render's back they called him "sitili" because he was reputed to have killed two African miners underground with the steel bit of a jack-hammer. The company accepted that he had acted in self-defence and had transferred him to Robinson Deep after the alleged incident. The men liked Render because he understood them, would joke with them, and would cajole the Mine Captain into laying on extra air-lines bringing delicious refrigerated dry air to the working places, where the rock was hot to the touch. Render told them exactly what he wanted doing and saw that they did it. Sometimes, in showing the drillers exactly where to drill, he would pick up the jack-hammer himself, handling the clumsy heavy machinery like a toy. He was an experienced miner who never shirked risky work or ever asked an African to do anything he wouldn't or couldn't do himself. Frequently he would distribute cigarettes to them. He was very unlike the white English men Makeleni had met previously in Nyasaland. One day, when Makeleni had absentmindedly begun work in the wrong place, Render shouted at him worse than his father-in-law with his furious face close to Makeleni's. Makeleni was really scared, but shortly afterwards when Render revisited his working place he joked with him and gave him a cigarette. "If you work hard and I get a good bonus, I'll look after you Kaffirs," was Render's philosophy – an excellent working relationship!

Sunday was a day of rest, to talk, to wash clothes, and to gather at the arena to watch and perhaps take part in the dances. This was rather humiliating for Makeleni and his friends because their traditional tribal dances were not very spectacular and the crowd would soon get bored watching them and start to chant: "Puma, puma, puma" – get out! "Puma zonke" – get out, all of you. So they had to shamble off and sit and watch the jumps and contortions of the others, the proud stamping, rattling, war dance of the Xhosas, the dancing to strange haunting horn music of some Tanganyika men, the (also pathetic) lonely dances of the sombreroed blanket boys from Basutoland, the clever and carefully rehearsed wellington dances, the various animal and hunting dances, and above all the disciplined war dance of the Swazis. Makeleni did not find friends among these different tribes; rather, with his own people, he would seek out newcomers from the country of the lake and get all the latest news.

Such had been his life, confined to the compound, strenuous, womanless, for about fourteen months now. He was stronger and fitter than he had ever been. He looked it and knew it. His savings would settle once and for all his debt to his father-in-law and leave some money over for new clothes and other luxuries to impress people at home, where his thoughts turned ever more frequently.

Then one day, Makeleni, now a gang leader, was crouching with Render at a place where two open stopes joined, leaving a wedge-shaped layer of yet unmined gold-bearing rock, the extraction of which would provide work for the following week or more. Suddenly, without warning, a splinter of rock flew off the rock face with a report like that of a gun and ricochetted between them down the stope. "Man, we've got a load on," said Render, and the next two days saw many extra log baulks placed just behind the working faces, where the familiar routine of drilling, blasting, and lashing was proceeding. Render personally supervised the siting of each hole drilled in the diminishing wedge of rock. The place was visited next day by the Mine Captain, who said that work should proceed despite Render's protestation that "It was a bastard, man."

It was noticeable that the new trainee mine geologist, a young Britisher who had once worked in Nyasaland near Makeleni's village, didn't linger in the place where they were now working.

The following day Makeleni was standing in the gallery below the stope not far from Render and the Mine Captain who was visiting again. He did not follow the heated argument that was going on between them, and consequently Makeleni was the first to notice the low-pitched pounding noise, steadily becoming louder and clearer. The two white men stared speechless at each other. Render was the first to recover his wits and dashed into the stope crying, "Puma, puma, zonke", but it was too late. The pounding became a terrifying hell of crashing and slashing of rock all around them.

Makeleni thought he was not hurt badly until he felt the warm soaking blood on his shirt spurting from his neck where a sharp splinter had neatly and painlessly sliced open his throat. He tried to crawl through the debris but realised he was trapped. As he died he tried to beg another dying man to be taken back and buried at his home in the country of the lake, but he couldn't speak for blood. From the now closed-up stope the dust oozed red, a red that did not distinguish between white and black.

That same afternoon, in a comfortable room, panelled with African hardwoods, on the grand second floor of the great square office building of dressed stone at 44 Main Street, an executive of the corporation sat talking with a visiting financier from abroad. He was explaining to the visitor how Main Street had actually been built along the outcrop of the main reef, when he paused abruptly. "Did you feel that one?" "No," the visitor replied, puzzled. "Ah, that was one of our earth tremors. We get two or three a day. If you're out walking you don't notice them. Even if you're sitting down quietly, you have to be used to them before you recognise them." "I didn't know Johannesburg was prone to earthquakes." "Oh Lord no, these are just caused by old mine workings settling and collapsing from time to time." "Old workings?", the visitor queried. "Yes, mostly old workings." "But not all old?", the visitor persisted. "Well, no, not all," was the reply.

Footnote: The average annual death-toll of workers in South African mines is not far short of a thousand, the vast majority of them black.

* * * * * * *

Sharpeville

Monday, 21st March 1960. 67 dead. 186 injured.

> "Demonstrators attacked the Police with assorted weapons including firearms. The demonstrators shot first, and the Police were forced to fire in self-defence."

The above quotation is part of a South African Government statement on the Sharpeville massacre issued via the South African High Commissioner in London, a Mr. van Rhyn. It is in fact a lie, a lie in the face of numerous eye-witness accounts of the actual course of events.

The demonstrators carried no firearms of any kind. The only "assorted weapons" that the police were able to produce were a few women's sun-shades and old men's walking sticks dropped by a fleeing crowd. There was no offensive behaviour at all. For example, no stones, the usual weapon of an unarmed rioting mob, were thrown. The police were never in any danger. They were inside a large rectangular enclosure which was surrounded by a strong stake and wire netting fence which remained unbroken. The police were well armed with their customary rifles, machine guns, and armoured cars, and were in fact impregnable.

A gate was opened at intervals to let cars carrying policemen and officers into the compound. A good-natured crowd made way for them without incident of any kind. Photographs taken shortly before the shooting show the white policemen at their ease, some of them with their backs to the crowd around the fence and only a few yards from it. It is impossible therefore to conclude that the crowd was hostile to the point of physical violence, and it is also impossible to ignore the evidence of hundreds of eye-witnesses on this crucial point.

A certain colonel Pienaar was in command of the police. In court, he denied on oath giving any order to fire. What can one think? Was he a liar, or was he not able to command the forces under him? It is, incidentally, a euphemism to call these forces policemen, which word has a different meaning in the English language.

So what happened? The truth is that a weapon *was* used by that crowd of Africans, on the afternoon of a warm sunny day, patiently waiting for a promised announcement on the first day of a general strike. The announcement had been promised for two o'clock. The weapon was very effective, too effective. It was an ironic cheer for the companies of armed men arrayed against them.

What actually happened next was in fact more horrifying to contemplate than a lying and incompetent officer or scared soldiers firing because they were afraid. The police were seized by a mass hysteria, based not on fear, but paradoxically on respect, for the disciplined patience of the Kaffirs, who were daring to flaunt their newly-found power of concerted industrial action in front of their faces. The firing, when it broke out, became uncontrollable. It continued for some appreciable time as an incredulous crowd, many of them women and children dressed in their best clothes, turned to flee. Photographs clearly show police climbing on to armoured vehicles in order to obtain better vantage points from which to spray a fleeing crowd in the back with fire from automatic weapons. The great majority of the killed and wounded were in fact shot in the back. As anyone accustomed to the use of firearms would confirm, the casualty figures of 67 dead and 186 seriously injured imply a great deal of shooting, and a great deal of shooting to kill.

Look again at the government statement, quoted verbatim. Is it common English usage to spell police with a capital P? I have to tell you that these capital Police are in large part recruited from a semi-literate poor-white Afrikaans population, whose life-style is based on white supremacy and inhumanity to Africans – "basskop".

However, if you had been content to sit back and receive the fat dividends on South African Kaffir gold shares, you could have reflected that stability was assured. Although there may be "regrettable incidents" such as Sharpeville – "grossly exaggerated", of course, and over-publicised by an "irresponsible" press – in the last analysis a ratio of five to one is not enough to overcome machine guns.

So much for democracy, justice, and human decency in the pre-Mandela South Africa that I knew, a state of affairs that has, alas, bequeathed a grim legacy to an uncertain future there.

Ambush

After the break-up of the Federation of Rhodesia and Nyasaland came the unilateral declaration of independence (UDI) by the white-dominated rump of Southern Rhodesia. This was accompanied by fine talk of the need to preserve "democracy, civilisation, and Christian values" there. During the ensuing outbreak of guerrilla war, several geologists were conscripted into the forces of the white government. It was considered that geologists' knowledge of the bush might be useful. One of these geologists was a colleague and close friend who was seldom disposed to speak of his war experiences which had left him prematurely aged.

The rain drops coldly from the tall trees at the edge of the virgin forest as night falls six thousand feet up in the eastern mountains. The quiet watchers discern a small group of men crudely dressed in torn khaki and animal skins loping smoothly along in single file on the narrow game path up through the winding valley of long grass. The men carry arms – a curious assortment of old muzzle-loaders, spears, and pangas (machetes). The watchers, more numerous, are similarly armed and dressed. One of them, their leader, has a new rifle captured only two months ago. The lonely cry of an early nightjar in the forest edge is echoed by one in the valley as the runners silently continue on.

Two miles back down the valley, moving nearly as quickly as the runners, is a column of uniformed men armed with rifles and automatic weapons. The column is led by two non-uniformed African men, apparently trackers, and four Europeans in khaki and soft jungle caps. They are very tired and stop to confer. "How many are they?" asks their leader again. He is a wiry man whose lined brown skin and manner suggest a long time spent in this tropical country. "Perhaps six, bwana, no more than eight." "You're sure?" "Sure, bwana." The leader turns to the three white soldiers. "Well, they'll stop for the night as soon as they reach some kind of shelter in the forest. It may be difficult to find them, but it's a chance of getting a prisoner." "So, we go on?" "Yes, as fast as possible." He turns to an African sergeant. "Take six fast men and go in advance. Try to make contact. Don't take risks until we catch you up. Just keep them pinned down." They move off and the others follow. An excitement ripples through them and gives them fresh energy, though the men look around them uneasily as they go.

Twenty minutes later there is a rustle among the watchers as the advance group comes into view proceeding warily but swiftly in the dusk to where the forest closes in on the valley. The leader of the watchers raises his hand and cautions the others to wait. The uniformed men below pass out of sight towards the deep gloom of the forest. The larger group can now be seen approaching at a fast march.

"Surprised we haven't heard anything," says their officer. "Looks like they've gone on into the forest. This could be a little messy." As he speaks, one of the white soldiers spins round and falls clutching his shoulder, simultaneously with the crack of a rifle shot. Further down the column there is a sudden screaming followed by automatic fire. The officer looks back, then runs forward only to see a man with a panga hacking at the profusely bleeding body of his tracker who is still alive. Unable to move his butchered limbs, he is looking at his killer. Regardless of his own instructions to take prisoners wherever possible, the officer cuts the slayer in two with automatic fire. Other automatic fire sweeps the grass and peters out. "Change to tracer." Night has come quickly and the one tracer in five of the automatic fire lights up the incongruously lonely valley. Again an answering crack of a rifle and a bullet narrowly misses its target. "Cease fire. They've only one rifle. We will advance and try to take prisoners. Advance."

The ambushers, realising that they are outnumbered and outgunned are already preparing to make off as the several parties now meet in a confused running engagement. In a few minutes of terror and confusion, sudden death, ghastly panga wounds, and near escapes, it is all over. Quiet descends again on the valley. A search in the grass reveals three dead and three wounded ambushers, for the loss of one dead tracker and five wounded of the government forces.

The three wounded prisoners are tied tightly with strips of losi (bark) peeled off some nearby mopani trees. Walking over to where they are lying in the flattened grass, the officer asks them: "We have the burning spear in our prison. Where is the lion? Tell us or you will die." The three prisoners, cold, dirty, their hair tied in spiky knots, and all with a look of horrifying vacantness in their eyes, are silent. With six revolver shots, the officer deliberately kills two of them, each one first with a shot in the abdomen, then the chest, then the head. The eyes of the third, a forced witness to these summary executions, now have an expression of deep vacant horror. "Speak or you too will die, with your penis cut off and stuck in your mouth and with a long sharp stake up your arse." No answer, so the wounded prisoner is later tied to a log over a fire and slowly burnt. "Give his balls a good toasting," says the officer. The prisoner says not a word. "Cut him down, we will try something else," says the officer, but the prisoner is already dead. His open eyes have retained the same expression till the end.

One of the young white soldiers vomits quietly in the grass. An older man, a conscript with a British accent, is disposed to argue with the officer. "Look here, my boy," the Rhodesian officer replies, "You still don't know these guerrillas, do you? You can't treat them like human beings. They are savages gone rotten."

So, it had finally come to this. My disillusion was already complete. I had seen the way things were going and decided that the time had come to quit. I did not feel allegiance to any sordid white-settler regime. Much later, I came across the closing words of Tolstoy's *The Kingdom of God is Within You*, written when he was sixty-five years young:

> A man need only awaken from the hypnotism of imitation in which he lives, and look soberly at what the State demands of him, in order not merely to refuse obedience, but to feel a fearful astonishment and indignation that men could address such demands to him.
>
> And that awakening may occur at any moment.

Amen. I ended up in newly independent Ghana.

* * * * * * *

A page of history

Hapless Congo has been independent for six bloody weeks. Events in that tragic country have suddenly become of international concern. On the recently enlarged apron of Accra airport stand huge American jets, Russian turbo-jets, British Comets, and – a touch of comic relief – some antediluvian British transports. Behind them on the approach a queue of yet more of the world's finest aircraft are waiting to take off as soon as refuelling and reloading are complete. Units of three battalions of the Ghana army are formed in companies waiting to board, the men smart and efficient-looking, crouching in lines led by either Ghanaian or British lieutenants. As each platoon in turn shoulders packs and rifles and then boards one of the waiting planes, a great cry arises from the tens of thousands of spectators, who form a massed backcloth of teeming colour to this extraordinary scene. Every twenty minutes or so a great plane laden to capacity with soldiers, food, fuel, and ammunition, screams down a runway also lined by singing and drumming crowds. Well into the night, made day by emergency spotlights, the crowds keep their vigil as the relief operation, so surely to prove successful, continues without cease.

From one of the returning planes emerges a stream of refugees, mainly white. They pass escorted by police to the little hotel across the road. They remain practically silent, but a few words of French reveal them to be Belgian. "Belgians," the cry goes up from the crowd, but it is quickly hushed when they see the shocked faces and staring eyes of the refugees, some of them clutching children. Were these dazed frightened people then the overlords of an immense and rich country? A mammy, overcome with emotion, tears streaming down her face, rushes past the police and tries to give a coloured cloth scarf to a child in the arms of its father. The child screams and the man recoils in terror. Mutually shocked, the mammy and the man stare at each other, before the police gently lead her away and the man walks on slowly, staring and uncomprehending.

That night the usual open-air dance at the Seaview is packed as Irish, Moroccan, and Swedish soldiers, also in transit to the Congo, join the multiracial throng of dancers. On the balconied patio, the band and its drummers beat out the rhythms of the *Highlife* dance. At times, the instrumentalists stop and all are moving to the rhythm of the drums alone, the old, old rhythm of Africa. The red lighthouse close by sends its recurrent beam over the scene, and every so often the sounds of music and laughter are temporarily drowned by the deep throbbing scream of labouring engines as yet another plane slowly gains height into the dying sea breeze and heads out over the Guinea Gulf to the Congo.

That afternoon an expectant House of Assembly in Accra had awaited the arrival of President Kwame Nkrumah, who was to make an important speech. The galleries were packed and displayed a cross section of Ghana, cosmopolitan and colourful. Many on this occasion were wearing the traditional dress of a toga for the men and a long skirt with tailored top for the women, all in riotous kente designs. Northerners, Nigerians, Malians could be distinguished by their different styles of dress and headwear. The private gallery was packed by foreign diplomats. Dispersed through the watchers were many Europeans, participating in the sense of occasion and enjoying life in this happy and tolerant African country, one of the first to become independent. Seating for the delegates to the Parliament was in the new horseshoe design, preferred by President Nkrumah (aka "Osagyefo" = Messiah) to the two-party opposition-bench system.

A roar of motor cycles, the dying scream of the sirens of the motorcade, and an answering thunderous tumult from the immense crowd outside drowned the welcoming drummers, and Osagyefo entered, only thirty-five minutes late. Eventually, there ensued a pregnant silence. I will always remember his opening words: "I come at a time of great danger for Africa; it is also the time of greatest hope."

I kept my thoughts to myself. I remembered my father telling me, as a young child, stories of the incredible atrocities committed in the name of the King of the Belgians (who *personally* owned the Congo at one time) on Africans there, working as virtual slaves in their own homeland. Later, I had read Conrad's *Heart of Darkness*. Now there was anarchy, murder and assassination in that unhappy country, organised on a scale which surely suggested a sinister purpose. Already, some revelations had emerged about the role of mining corporations, which controlled the rich mines of Congo's Katanga province, in engineering Katanga's secession under the puppet Tschombe and in the murder of President Patrice Lumumba. Although the UN relief effort was substantial and to outward appearances supported by all, could it be that powerful vested interests were behind all the trouble?

Curiously, some years later, while living in Spain, I met up in a Madrid bar with two Britishers who claimed to have been high-ranking mercenaries with Tschombe and, later, Mobutu. They were disposed to talk, and readily confirmed what I had long suspected about the assassination of Lumumba and the "plane accident" that befell Dag Hammarskyold. They were also quick to point out, as some kind of justification for their bloody work, the extent of underhand British involvement reaching to the heart of government, despite the latter's outward show of support for the United Nation's intervention in the Congo. They referred, inter alia, to those numerous members of MacMillan's cabinet who were known to hold substantial stakes in the holding company for Katanga mines, and to the organised and successful rubbishing of United Nation's Conor Cruise O'Brien by the right-wing press in Britian. I imagine that much of what they said contained elements of the truth.

I realise now that what we were witnessing in poor Congo was the raw cutting edge of the phenomenon called "neocolonialism". Neocolonialism (cynical exploitation of a Third World country without any of the responsibilities that a former colonial power might have assumed) has since learned to be a bit more subtle! Alas, Nkrumah's heartfelt dream of "hope" for Black Africa was never to be realised.

* * * * * * *

The one-party System

West African tours were short, about fifteen months on average, with a generous three months leave, not even counting time spent on the relaxing voyage home by ship. So I had plenty of time to look up old friends in

Oxford and elsewhere. I remember one evening going to a meeting of the "Free Africa Now" society.

In the lecture room of a modern Oxford college named after a famous 19th century liberal philanthropist a small but expectant audience is waiting. They seem to be a serious group of people, lacking some of the cheerful extrovertness of a usual college society gathering. Many, like myself, appear to have come singly and are looking around appraising the others. These include several Africans wearing long college scarves and quite a few young women, not all one would say college types. One unmistakable college lass, complete with tweed suit and spectacles, evidently the secretary, is handing out leaflets concerning the next meeting. Some rather retiring young men students and a few older people, including some determined looking middle-aged women, complete the ensemble.

Perhaps their seriousness can be excused. "Africa emergent" is a worthy and topical theme, appealing alike to conscience and sentiment in the current "wind of change". Who knows what yet unimagined iniquities of former colonialists, white people like most of the audience but clearly of a different genre, will be revealed tonight? The visiting speaker is to be a junior minister from one of the less well-known and very recent republics of West Africa. The audience prepares to be broad-minded, throw aside racial prejudices, and lend a friendly ear to the speaker, being careful to avoid any hint of patronising.

A man, possibly in his late thirties, with a weak but friendly face, watery blinking eyes, dirty baggy trousers, and unkempt long blond hair, shambles in. He is followed by the striking upright tall figure of an African, impeccably dressed in a tailored charcoal-grey suit. The latter's complexion is dark brown rather than black and his handsome features suggest an Arab strain. These two take their places on the platform and are evidently the chairman and speaker. The chairman, blinking benignly at the audience, scrambles to his feet and says how honoured Oxford is to welcome the speaker, who is in Britain to raise credit for a proposed new national airline, but has found time to come here tonight, etc. He adds that the minister will speak in his excellent French which most will be able to follow, but that he, the chairman, will give a précis at intervals as the talk progresses. The chairman sits down, but after a hasty whispered conversation with the minister, rises again, blinking more genially than ever, to explain that the subject of the talk, which he had forgotten to mention, will be the one-party system of government.

The minister rises. Intending to speak without notes, he pauses to survey, one could almost say to command, the audience, who are expectantly hushed. He begins to speak softly and fluently, even arrestingly, albeit incomprehensibly to many of those present, and evidently warms to his theme. After some time, the chairman, half rising, makes a gargling noise and says he had better translate. Monsieur, he says, would like to clear up some misapprehensions about the one-party system in his country, about which there had been mistaken comments made in the British press. First, Monsieur would like to make it quite clear that it is really the truest form of democracy. Obviously so, because the one party represents everybody.

We learn in the next forty-five minutes or so, that an opposition party is really unnecessary when a country is united for freedom and progress. Moreover, it would be a waste of educated manpower, already in grave short supply, due to the failure of the former colonial government to educate more Africans to university level. Indeed, an opposition would become a rallying point for criminal elements in society and, after some defining of terms with the chairman who smiles benevolently, neocolonialists.

No, the one-party system is democratic and just, because every important piece of legislation is debated at village level. The local party organisers then convene to give their views to MPs who then reflect these views in parliamentary debate. Could this be rivalled anywhere else in the so-called democratic countries? The speaker goes on to explain that there is a truly African precedent for the one-party system. This is in tribal meetings, where the chief, by custom consigned to silence in debate, hears all the litigants, listens to elders, and only then gives his decision which is final and binding, a decision which must however express the sense of the meeting.

This reference to tradition obviously pleases the audience in this old university town. The speaker has made a good impression and resumes his seat, gazing impassively before him. Genuine applause and then the chairman, after making a deprecatory allusion to his own command of French, which privately he considers excellent, asks for questions.

Immediately, an African student is on his feet. Would the minister kindly explain why twelve members of the former opposition party are in prison, please, in his democracy. The speaker gravely replies that the questioner is incorrect as there is no opposition party. Some people had been found guilty by the high court of treason, but by the leniency of the president their death sentences were reduced to fifteen years imprisonment. Was the questioner referring to these men?

The questioner, very dark-skinned, now asks if the minister could explain recent border incidents involving the terrorisation of the questioner's tribe in a neighbouring country. The speaker gently reproves the questioner, saying that this was not the subject of his talk, but he will reply. The fact is that some Iwe people in the questioner's country were merely demonstrating their love of African unity and their desire to be incorporated in the minister's country, with which they felt a spiritual affinity. Troops had been to the frontier, not in any way to threaten the neighbouring country, but merely to keep order and indeed preserve the existing boundary. It was quite untrue that Iwe agents-provocateurs were sent from his, the minister's, country, to foment discontent.

The questioner seems to want to ask something else, but the chairman declares that the minister should perhaps take some questions from others in the audience. This is not before the persistent questioner is heard to say something about the curious coincidence of all government members being appointed from the same tribe as the minister. Eventually the questioner sits down with an expression of sullen disbelief, and endures the hostile glances of the audience who clearly seem to feel that he is a trouble-maker.

The meeting ends on a gentler note, after an unexceptional young man, apparently an economist, asks about economic progress. This gives the minister the chance to conclude with a few statistics. For example, under the French colonial regime, for very many years only about 60% to 70% of the groundnut crop was first grade, but since the state marketing board was set up, the percentage of first-grade nuts has risen rapidly to 95%. This was undeniably progress, although it had still not been sufficiently recognised by European buyers.

The minister remains impassive as the chairman bumbles and fumbles the meeting to a close.

* * * * * * *

The Cocoa Farm

On the ground, I have to say that reality was a little different to the fantasy retailed in an Oxford lecture theatre.

From the village on the car road a track leads north through hot corn fields on cleared land with only an occasional forest tree left standing. Then a path branches right towards the wooded hills and rises slowly, soon gaining the welcome shade of the forest. After two miles or so and passing many small forking paths leading to cocoa farms the path strikes steeply upward. After some exertion one arrives at Kwasikrom, the village of Kwasi. The few houses, built soundly of massive sun-baked clay bricks with good corrugated iron roofs, are right at the highest point of the ridge, where one at once feels a slight but immensely refreshing breeze. An unusual situation perhaps, an hour's steady grind from the village, but water is close at hand in a tiny but perennial spring at the foot of some white crags. One could guess that the site had been chosen by a self-contained man of character, and one would be right.

Kwasi, the son of the first Kwasi who settled here some sixty years ago, is now himself a man of late middle-age, serene and squarely built, and still quite fit. He is working now with slow, strong, and adept movements, splitting the large yellow cocoa pods with a fearsome-looking machete, and packing the nests of cocoa seeds amongst their white sticky matrix in groups on the ground under banana leaves, where they will ferment and more easily release the individual seeds. Further on down the other side of the hill, two of his sons and a younger brother are picking the ripe pods from the boles of the cocoa trees. At intervals, they slowly come up the hill to their father bringing loads of fresh pods. Kwasi's wife, rather aged and bent, having put some freed cocoa seeds out to dry on matting between the houses of the hamlet, is working in her untidy tiny garden. The garden is viewed with a mixture of tolerant amusement and genuine admiration by the rest of the family. It produces a constant supply of peppers, egg-plants, tomatoes, and numerous other kinds of seasonings for the pot. A good-looking young woman, wife of one of the sons, swings down the hill to the spring with a baby tied to her back, blinking and clutching at the empty air.

One can perhaps excuse Kwasi for being a contented man. The numerous goats and chickens do not stray from their hilltop home, and his experiment in keeping a small sty of pigs has proved successful. The family does not lack meat. His oranges, from trees that give the impression of growing wild among the rocks by the spring, are renowned as the sweetest in the district. Among the cocoa trees there are plentiful yams and other tubers to make good fu-fu.

When I first passed this way to look at the curious white rocks, I must say I did not at first appreciate how intensively this forest country can be farmed, and how self-sufficient good farmers can make themselves, and how varied are forest products. For example, a little further back down the hill, where the tiny rivulet from the spring disappears into a flat area, marshy in the rains, there are enormous clumps of bamboo, almost as high as some of the forest trees, adjacent to a grove of thickly jostling plantains. Each year, some of the bamboo is carefully cut, paying considerable respect to the numerous snakes that infest it, chopped into four-foot lengths, split in two, pointed at one end, and used to renew the fencing the protects two small corn fields from wild pig. No wonder that, having made friends with Kwasi and his family, I was in the habit of revisiting their farm on the occasional weekend. Though only some thirty miles inland, it was a world apart from the bustle, squalor, and heat of Accra. Moreover, theirs was a lifestyle that I instinctively took to.

Cocoa, Kwasi sighs, cocoa needs hard work at certain times of the year. But it is cocoa that provides the cash to buy cloth for the womenfolk, a radio, a gun, and provides bride money for the boys. If there is a year when some cash is left over, it is taken to Accra market to buy gold, the only form of saving practised by the family. The cocoa farm leaves plenty of other times for leisure and the important things of life, such as visitings, weddings, and observing the proper customs and ceremonies, including the annual parading of the nearby village's lingham fertility stone (which the white missionaries, comfortably ensconced on another cool hill not far away, had attempted to proscribe).

But lately, since independence? Kwasi would admit that independence was a good thing in principle, to see all those wonderful new buildings in Accra, not much happening locally, but perhaps give the government time? Strange that so many members of the government were once well-known criminals and thugs. Osagyefo really must do something about them.

In the meantime, there are difficulties. The price paid to farmers for each bag of cocoa has been greatly reduced. Now this is surprising, as did not the CPP tell us before independence that the British were stealing money from the farmers by paying too little for the cocoa? Also, now that the government buys the cocoa, it is difficult to get the money until nearly a whole year has passed, and only then after giving a suitable dash to the government agent. In contrast to this, the British buyers or their agents used to come with cash to the village. Also, six shillings on each bag of cocoa is now deducted by the government in tax, and another six shillings for the "development". The difference between these is that one gets back the latter after six years. [This didn't happen; Ghana became bankrupt, having spent within six years the three hundred million pounds of cocoa-fund money bequeathed them by the British!] Also, cocoa sacks are scarce, and it is necessary to give further bribes and drinks to the government agents at the depot in order to obtain them. However, it is still cocoa, and cocoa alone, that provides cash. Kwasi sighs again.

At this moment, there is a cry from the mother answered by the girl at the spring – a stranger, a stranger from the government. Kwasi sends a son to collect the others, and all proceed to the hamlet. The stranger, dressed in a white shirt and long black trousers, has been given a chair and some cool spring water. He is a little man, with an intelligent bulging forehead, largely obscured by a black and white check cap and thick black horn-rimmed spectacles. From his speech, akin enough to Kwasi's, it is apparent that he is from the coast. He is accompanied by two illiterate northern labourers dressed in government khaki, who are now lying sprawled in the shade. "Who are these people?" asks the stranger. "These are my brother and my sons," replies Kwasi. "I need only talk with you. I have come to inspect for swollen shoot." "You may talk with us all, we are all from here," Kwasi insists. The stranger scowls. "We saw swollen shoot on some of your trees on the way up. Why have you not reported it?" "No one came last year or the year before to inspect us," says Kwasi. This seems to annoy the stranger, who raises his voice and squeals: "I am a big man. I have a big job. Do you think I have time to visit each farm and each tree every year?"

Kwasi reflected how the stranger's British predecessor and his trusted men used to do precisely this every year. They inspected every single cocoa tree on the farm, quietly and firmly insisted on cutting down any infected trees, burning all twigs and branches, painting and disinfecting all the surrounding trees, and arranging government compensation on the spot. The British forestry officer had sat down and eaten with them, and quietly explained how the diseased cocoa trees would surely die anyway. Though they could continue to bear cocoa pods for five or six years after the first sign of swollen shoot, during this period they would infect many other cocoa trees which would also die in turn. Even carrying the cocoa pods from a diseased tree through the forest would infect other cocoa trees on the way. Though the compensation was modest, Kwasi had believed the Britisher, and every year his sons would accompany him back to the road carrying gifts of eggs, oranges, a chicken, and yams. It was indeed part of the year's round, and after the early years when a lot of cocoa trees had to be destroyed when swollen shoot had first manifested itself in the area, and Kwasi had been angry and upset about it, fewer and fewer had to be cut down each year, and the Britisher had thus talked true.

So Kwasi said nothing, and waited for the stranger to continue. The stranger demands, "You know you must cut down your infected trees." "Don't you want to come and see for yourself?" asks Kwasi. "No, we are too busy," says the stranger, "but if we see swollen shoot again, you will be in big trouble." "What about the compensation?" asks Kwasi. "Very well, sign this," says the stranger. "Father," says one of the sons who has been to school, "Nothing is written here; we don't know how many trees." "Sign this form if you want the compensation," screams the stranger. The son reflects that his grandfather would have taken considerable pleasure in nailing the cheeks of this coastal scum to a tree and after a suitable interval killing him in the traditional manner by driving another nail into his head. But there is nothing to do, but watch his father laboriously sign his name at the foot of the empty page. "That is good," says the stranger, "I shall go now, but what about my dash? Maybe I can help you in the future." No one had thought of a present for the stranger, but recollecting themselves, a chicken and some eggs are found, and some money reluctantly handed over.

The stranger walks off down the hill with the two labourers who have contributed nothing to the events of the day. Kwasi sighs – cocoa.

The cumulative effects of widespread corruption were indeed to destroy the economy of Ghana, once the richest country in Black Africa, within just a few years after independence.

* * * * * * *

The Leaving

In many respects work in the Ghana Geological Survey was very pleasant. It had been one of the best in British colonial Africa with an impressive list of discoveries to its credit. As with many other Geological Surveys, a good part of its work had to do with the vital, albeit unglamorous, job of providing safe water supplies for people in rural areas. The HQ when I arrived was in the sleepy coastal village of Saltpond overlooked by an old slaving fort. The Survey enjoyed excellent relations with the people of Saltpond. The big event of the year was the annual football match against our old rivals, the "Post and Telegraph".

I well remember the first game I witnessed. Our team was strengthened by some good players brought in from drilling crews in the bush. Theirs was (unfairly) strengthened by good players brought in from the nearby town of Cape Coast. The sidelines were roughly defined by the spectators, who were held at bay by being continually threatened with palm-fronds brandished by the linesmen. Footwork was good, although players seemed to be more concerned with giving the impression they had come off best in tackles, or had been tackled unfairly, than actually getting the ball towards the net. The pitch sloped rather steeply towards the beach. As a consequence, the PT team, playing downhill, had scored three goals by half-time, and we were nil. During the interval, Mr Addy, senior man in our General Office, told our players to unselfishly pass the ball more, and Mr Mensah, Librarian, told them to pass less and shoot. Mr Addy, a portly little gentleman, adopted the same tone of command as he used in the office. Mr Mensah emphasized his point with a walking stick. As a result of their excellent advice, we scored twice in the second half, even though the strengthening sea breeze was beginning to counter the advantage of the slope. The final result, 2-3, was considered reasonable in view of the dishonesty of the other side and the referee's lack of impartiality. Each time a player fell over a free kick had been awarded, and their side had fallen over more. The winning side was cheered off the field in a mammy-wagon. Afterwards, we went to bathe in the gentle surf as usual before a (moral) victory party in the evening. It was all very relaxed.

But there were some disquieting features. The senior staff were the former colonial geologists, now content with occupying their last year or two in pushing files around in the office before quitting and drawing their pensions. The young geologists, hired on contract terms like myself, did the arduous bushwork working in individual field parties in difficult terrain, often with inadequate supervision and back-up from those who should have been providing these. I was relatively fortunate in having a post that allowed me to spend time at HQ but with any amount of liaison work in the field. I particularly enjoyed working among Ewe people in the misty hills of Trans-Volta Territory which somehow reminded me of Wales. Busy but interesting. Then we were moved into a posh new office in Accra. Bureaucracy, government meddling, and corruption all began to proliferate.

By government standards, I suppose we had been administratively understaffed before. In the event, we acquired a new senior accountant and increased staff at the time of our move into Accra. Not long afterwards, I noticed that my laboratory staff had become listless and tended to spend time sitting with their heads in their hands. Eventually, I discovered that they were all in debt to the accountant who doled out their monthly wages!

He had contrived to lend them money, well secured of course on their next month's wages, at 25% interest per month. Now I realised the reason for the two queues outside the accountant's office every monthly pay-day. The system worked like this. Suppose you were earning $9 a month and found you were spending nearer $10, and suppose over a period of a few months you had borrowed a total of $4. After emerging from the first queue, you would have received your pay less the loan plus its accrued interest, that is to say $9, less $4 principal and $1 interest. So you found yourself now looking not at $9, but $4. You then joined the second queue and borrowed say $6, so that you would again have $10 to spend during the month. All very well, but the repayment on $6 next month will be $7.50, so very quickly your financial situation accelerates into hopelessness. Now 25% may not sound enormous if you urgently need money, but with interest compounded at 25% per month a debt of say $10 becomes something like $140 in a year! [Work it out and see!] No wonder my men were depressed.

This kind of usury became commonplace in the government service. When I had at last cottoned on, I rescued my own men by means of a stiff lecture cum explanation, paying off their debt to the accountant with witnesses, and having them pay me back interest-free at $1 per month. Not one of them let me down. Needless to say, I was not popular with the accountant. My regret was that I couldn't undertake to do the same for the many among the rest of the men at the survey who were being loan-sharked in this manner.

Government felt, understandably, that the Geological Survey should have a Ghanaian Director. Our best man was in America working on a doctorate and was summarily brought home. He had been a very credible field geologist, then earned a master's degree in Britain, and had done a second tour of field work, again of a high standard. He was a man of the highest motives and integrity, but was catapulted into a very uncomfortable position indeed. He was genuinely upset at the climate of corruption which had permeated us all. For example, one of his first formal acts as Director happened to be to preside over a modest party to mark the 50th anniversary of the Survey. After a decision on an appropriate amount of whisky, he was genuinely amazed to learn that this could most economic-ally be bought through a CPP agent who arranged the smuggling of it from Dahomey thus avoiding proper government taxes, even though the government *was*, in effect, the one party of the CPP – the Convention People's Party!

In common with other Government departments, we had a CPP liaison officer appointed to the Survey. I found him to be a reasonable enough fellow and, at times, a useful "Mr. Fix-It", but I am pretty sure our new Ghanaian Director did not appreciate his presence. Our new Director was also embarrassed by not having completed his doctorate, particularly as one or two pushy young Ghanaian geologists had both doctorates and political connections. At one stage, he wanted to submit work that I had completed in Ghana for his own doctorate thesis. Although flattered, I demurred and advised him against doing this. Eventually, he just took to styling himself Doctor.

Despite its overpowering presence, the government, alias CPP, felt insecure, especially after a few bombs were exploded in Accra. One of them, incidentally, took off part of the bottom of our storeman who could well afford the reduction in weight. As a counter-insurgency measure, the bungalows of all expatriates were to be searched for weapons. This, of course, was absurd as expatriates steered right away from internal political matters. An officer and small detachment of men duly turned up at my bungalow. I had an extremely docile cross-bred collie, who for the first time in his life, taking umbrage at the sight of so many soldiers, barked menacingly. Despite being armed with rifles with fixed bayonets they were all scared stiff. My steward Abraham picked up the dog and with great presence of mind put it in the storeroom. The officer and I sat down to a beer and privately agreed on the futility of suspecting people like myself of any complicity in the sundry protests and bombings that were going on. Abraham gave iced water from the fridge to the soldiers who perfunctorily searched the bungalow. The one place they never looked was the storeroom! Just as well: as well as the dog it contained two crates of contraband whisky, which would probably have been confiscated. It could equally well have contained a cache of arms and bombs for all they knew!

Abraham and his wife had a most beautiful and well cared for little girl, Mimi, aged about four. We all adored her. One day I came home in the early evening to find Abraham not there. I was told that he had been at hospital all day with Mimi who had suffered a bad burn to her arm. When I got to Korle Bu hospital after dusk, I found a Dickensian scene of confusion, with Mimi apparently no nearer receiving attention than when she and Abraham had arrived in the morning. A doctor noticed us and called Mimi over for treatment. Mimi would be OK. I was relieved but upset to realise that it was my presence as a white person that had accelerated things – so many others, some in worse shape, still waited patiently. A couple of years after leaving Ghana I received a letter from Abraham saying that Mimi had taken sick and died. This news affected me deeply and I have never forgotten that lovely child.

Once while driving in Accra I was stopped by a policeman who alleged some offence or other and demanded money on the spot. This happened all the time to Ghanaian drivers. I was really indignant that he thought he could pull this one on me and gave him such an earful that the poor fellow retreated.

Another driving incident in which one thing led to another was far more serious. I had stopped just in time to avoid hitting a black policeman dressed entirely in black who was standing in the middle of the Accra coastal road at night. We were both a bit shaken. He recovered enough to point a finger at me and say he was going to charge me. For my part, I figured that my quick reactions had probably saved him from serious injury or worse. In any event, I put out my lights and took off, thinking that this would be the best way to avoid trouble, as I had a passenger whose identity might have been sensitive. Unfortunately, the reason for the policeman's suicidal presence in the middle of the road was that he had been attempting to allow two lorryloads of police to enter the main road. This they promptly did and took off in pursuit of me. The leading lorry failed to make the corner where I had turned by the post office and rammed the side of the building. Some of the police jumped out and came running and shouting like the Keystone Cops up the short road to the roundabout where I was halted by traffic. Seeing them coming, I took off although I did not have the right of way, causing tail-end collisions by the sound of it. I figured I was done for, but luckily no one had taken my number in the confusion. Life was seldom dull in West Africa. I regret to say that understandable disrespect for corrupt and incompetent police became coupled with disrespect for the law in such matters as illicit diamond-dealing and illicit transactions in hard currencies.

Finding myself with a lot of time in town, for some time I helped with *The Young Pioneers*, a kind of official youth movement. I undertook scouting activities with them and was shocked to realise that some of the youngsters had never once in their lives been outside the slummy environs of Accra. Here was I, an expatriate, doing what I could to teach African children about their own country! I once took six mammy-wagon loads of them on a hilarious weekend tour including a visit to the Nsuta opencast manganese mine where the manager was most welcoming. Unfortunately, perhaps inevitably, the movement became increasingly politicized. At one point, a voluble but ignorant senior government official insisted that I train youngsters to become geologists. He took great umbrage when I pointed out that, although I could attempt to interest some of them in geology among many other things, any formal geological training would have to be achieved in college.

One day, I received a phone call from someone in government asking what "reclamation" work on a mine entailed. Now I had been involved in reclamation work on old gold mines in Southern Rhodesia, and very nasty and unpleasant work it is too, involving pumping out and making safe muddy old workings, sampling, and further development, all with a view to resuming mining. After explaining all this I opened the morning paper. The headlines talked of the overseas operators of gold mines in Ghana (having become exasperated with trying to work in an atmosphere of bribery and corruption) threatening to pull out, abandon their mines, and "reclaim" any salvageable mining machinery and plant. Quite the opposite meaning of the term reclamation! So, I had to phone back to the caller who admitted that he had been rather perplexed at my original explanation! The upshot was that afternoon I found myself, in the absence of our Director who was out of town, in a high-powered cabinet committee meeting. It was decided there and then to nationalise all gold mines. Prices were fixed for the takeover of shares of the several companies involved. I was quite likely the only one present at that meeting who, armed with the sure knowledge of the future take-over price, did not make a financial killing. The Geological Survey was later called on to supply expertise for running the mines, although we had made it clear from the outset that this was not within our sphere of competence, as we were essentially a field, not a mining, organisation. Later, I was called upon, and refused, to put my name to false figures of reserves.

Things were getting to the point where it was becoming difficult, if not impossible, to do the technical job I was being paid for. The crunch for me finally came over a relatively small matter, small that is in financial terms though not in personal terms.

We had a labourer from northern Ghana blinded in a blasting accident. He had been awarded compensation of $140. The people paying him had got him alone and had persuaded him to take just $40 but to make his mark for the $140. Otherwise, they threatened, he would receive nothing. He had been intimidated and had acquiesced in the crime against himself. Afterwards, he realised that he had given away his future life. $140 doesn't sound much, but it would have bought him a wife. $40 wouldn't go that far. He told his story to one of our geologists, who had it typed out and witnessed. He sent it in to me.

What was I do to? Such occurrences were regrettably commonplace. The cynical nature of this one made my mind up for me. I went to see the Crown Attorney and took the statement with me. He read it and said he would prosecute. I asked him how any prosecution could succeed as there was only the testimony of an illiterate blind labourer. He replied that the labourer would very probably be believed as he would not have had the nerve to invent the incident. I respected him for his common sense, but at that point I picked up the statement and got up to leave his office. He attempted to stop me, but I think he realised my motive and what I was going to do. In the event, I went straight back to the Geological Survey office, and threatened to let the prosecution go ahead unless the labourer received his money forthwith. In less than half an hour, our beloved Senior Accountant was on his way by road to Cape Coast where he contacted the Paying Officer (who belonged to the same coastal tribe) and the labourer got his money. I do not know to what extent, indeed if any, some of our own survey staff may have been involved in the original fraud, but my part in the affair did not endear me to some.

So, disillusioned again, I quit, again, and this time left Black Africa for good. It was a time of great unhappiness for me. My memories of West Africa in particular were clouded by having seen how corruption was destroying a nation and the lives of its friendly happy extrovert people. I thought, indeed I still think, of the friendship and undeserved loyalty I had received from so many people in Africa.

I felt shattered and spent nearly the whole month of May quietly recuperating in Switzerland – very much between seasons as regards tourism, but a pleasant Spring in a clean neutral country with no pressures. It was during this period that I began to experience the first of many vivid memory flash-backs. These came into my consciousness unbidden and in great detail. Though I had kept very little in the way of a diary in Africa, I began to note these memories down in an exercise book at the time and a few of them have become the above little episodes and vignettes.

The "tape" of my "African awakening" and subsequent events in Africa has never been erased from my mind and will be with me till I die.

There was a glut of British geologists looking for jobs at this time, many of similar age and comparable experience to myself, having quit Africa for varying reasons. A few managed to find professional work. Nigel Baird, for example, a pleasant enough chap but not with a great deal between the ears in my opinion, landed an attractive survey cum teaching position. Nothing doing for me, and I became a vagabond.

PART III PILGRIMAGE

And when old words die out on the tongue, new melodies break forth from the heart, and where the old tracks are lost, new country is revealed with its wonders.

from the *Gitanjali* by Rabindranath Tagore

We are the pilgrims, master; we shall go
Always a little further; it may be
Beyond that last blue mountain barred with snow,
Across that angry or that glimmering sea.

James Elroy Flecker

We shall not cease from exploration and the end of all our exploring will be to arrive where we started and know the place for the first time.

T. S. Eliot

Vagabond years

For the next two and a half years I travelled around the Mediterranean, migrating like the birds, south in winter to Morocco, Egypt and the Levant, north to Yugoslavia and France in summer with brief visits to Britain and elsewhere. Of the several countries I visited, most time was spent in Spain. I didn't know my vagabondage was going to last that long, but one thing led to another. During this whole period I had only three months of conventional work as a geologist. This involved leading an expedition to the area of the ancient emerald mines of Sikait in the rock desert of Upper Egypt between the Nile and the Red Sea.

Seemingly purposeless at the time, I realise now that all this restless travel marked the beginning of a pilgrimage. It is, indeed, not the attainment of a journey's end, but the experiences one meets with along the way that determine the quality of a pilgrimage. A man may know what he flees from, but not what he seeks.

There were periods between travel when time stood still for me as in a dream during lengthy stays in three cities: Dubrovnik, Sevilla, and Jerusalem. The only other place which I found later that could compare with these was Katmandu. Sadly, all have suffered since. Dubrovnik has been the scene of crimes not merely against living humanity but also against the heritage of humanity. Sevilla has lost much of its charm and has seen an amazing growth in street crime. Jerusalem was far preferable when I knew it first as an Arab city, evocatively bringing to mind the ambience of times when the prophets of three religions had walked its streets. Katmandu has become transformed by tourism. It saddens me that no one now can have the privilege of knowing places such as these as they once were.

My stays in Spain included times when my journey partook of a character obviously akin to a pilgrimage. Not only did I spend two whole Easters enjoying Semana Santa and the ensuing Feria in Sevilla, but one hot July I followed the medieval pilgrimage route from the Pyrenees to Santiago.

Once I sought a western city, lost in legends, mist, and rainbows.

In the Pyrenees I had passed flocks of sheep led by wise belled goats on their way up to enjoy summer pastures, just as flocks had done for a thousand years or more. Like the hundreds of thousands, indeed millions, of earlier pilgrims who had followed this route centuries before me, I marvelled at the ancient bridges of Puente de la Reina and Puente Orbigón, and at the amazing Romanesque architecture of the many churches on the route, with their flamboyant carvings and touches of Mozarabic here and there and even hints of earlier Celtic themes. I ran with the bulls through the streets of Pamplona on the feast day of San Fermín, albeit very nervously and in a prudent manner. I pursued the lonely pilgrim route through once-important towns such as Estella now lying in decayed ruins, and across the searing wheat-lands of the meseta where I pitied the villagers for their thin crops. In León city I joined a procession of desperate peasants, their faces as desiccated and furrowed as their land, on their way to the cathedral in order to pray for rain to relieve the drought. I remember vividly still the magnificent disciplined singing of the choir and the impassioned singing of the congregation, all in the miraculous late-afternoon light filtered by the stained-glass windows of this lovely cathedral. In one obscure village church I was screamed at by a dirty hysterical priest about the iniquities of Henry the Eighth. Still frothing at the lips after his tirade, he rather spoilt the effect by begging for a duro (three pence) with insistent hand gestures like a chimpanzee. I gave him half a duro which pleased him greatly.

More by good luck than management I contrived to arrive in Santiago on the eve of the celebration of Saint James (Santiago). Over the last few kilometres from Lavacola people encouraged me on with gifts of milk, bread, and honey. It was well after dusk when I arrived at the city centre. The tourist office had remained open, even though they had no rooms left to send people to on this the busiest night of their year. But noticing my travel-stained condition and (quaintly!) idiomatic Spanish they kindly directed me to a fourth-class pension, a category never recommended to foreigners. Amazingly, it was right in the centre of the city on the corner of the Via Sacra overlooking the great south door of the cathedral. The overnight charge of 15 pesetas had been doubled to thirty (16 pence) in honour of the occasion. But the pension turned out to be free of bedbugs and I could not have been better pleased. At dawn the following morning I pressed inside the cathedral with a great multitude to witness the swinging of the Botafumeiro (an enormous censer) across the transepts and was given a small medallion by a suspicious priest: "Did you come here as a pilgrim?" "Yes, father," I replied humbly. Though not a Catholic, I certainly felt I had earned it.

Much of my time in Spain was based on Madrid. I escaped every weekend I was there in winter to ski in the Sierra de Guadarrama and I revisited the Sierra on long walks in summer alone with alpine flowers. Several times I visited the much lonelier high mountains and plateau of the Gredos west of Avila. On the way there I remember well an old posada floored with flagstones and rushes. On entering one had to wait to accustom one's eyes to the smoky darkness before sitting down to nourishing bowls of soup ladled out of an immense black pot over the open fire. In the Gredos I enjoyed the sight of high valleys absolutely covered by small daffodils in late Spring. In summer, I camped in that same area with shepherds and talked with them in the cool nights around fires replenished with armfuls of broom. Another time I bivouacked overnight also with shepherds underneath an arch of the great Roman bridge at Salamanca, the bridge to which vehicles *over* 16 tons weight are now diverted! "Este puente estaba aqui quando Christo andaba por el mundo", one of the shepherds proudly said (This bridge was here when Christ walked the earth). I read voraciously and particularly enjoyed the works of Garcia Lorca, Antonio Machado, and that great man Unamuno. All of this was as much of a pilgrimage as the formal one to Santiago.

And there were a great many more incidents which I found touching in one way or another. Once, while travelling in the Mancha, I made for some trees. These surrounded a small farmhouse and an open circular stone cistern, the water of which was replenished by a mule walking round in a circle pumping up water from the adjacent well. The man and his wife proudly indicated their two hectares of irrigated land and their only child, a comely girl in her early twenties. They had no son. All, they said jokingly, could be mine if I stayed. I must say I lingered while she washed and caressed my shoulders by the cistern with delicious cool water. Were they joking?!

Once I found myself on the daily bus from Riaño to Cangas. The narrow road crosses the then little-visited Picos de Europa range, in part along the narrow gorge of the Rio Sella. I was offered a seat, if I wished, on top of the single-decker bus. The seat turned out to be an unanchored bench in among the luggage with a guard-rail no more than fifteen inches high. The only other person who opted for the top was a small intense man wearing a black beret who, unlike many Spaniards, took a deep and intelligent interest in the countryside as we travelled. He was very well-informed and sensitive and turned out to be the well-known writer Cela. The journey was spectacular, not to say hair-raising in places. If only some latter-day EEC bureaucrat concerned with safety regulations could have seen us hanging on for dear life, pointing and talking away!

Another time I was walking in the central Pyrenees. I was heading, optimistically, towards Monte Perdido, but by early afternoon it was obvious I was not going to make the peak by a long chalk. As I turned for a final look at the mountain, I looked down at my feet and suddenly realised I was walking on a carpet of edelweiss. This is the only time I have seen this flower growing so profusely in the wild. Never once in my travels in Spain did I visit hideous tourist traps like the Costa del Sol.

During the Franco regime, the armed state police known as the Guardia Civil could be extremely brusque with their own people, especially left-wingers, and indeed with those extrañeros whose behaviour may have stepped outside conventional Spanish limits. However, if one went one's way quietly and courteously, manifested an intelligent interest in the country, and spoke some reasonable Spanish, they were generally very helpful indeed.

The only occasion they were brusque with me was when I had gone to visit the wonderful 9th century palace of Naranco near Oviedo in northern Spain. Despite my polite protests, and without any attempt at explanation, they kept me right away from the building which I had come so far to see. Then, a limousine swept up and a lady stepped out. She noticed my somewhat indignant figure, realised I was harmless, beckoned me over, and we spent some time looking at the building alone together and chatting. The charming, cultivated, and knowledgeable lady whose company I was sharing was Carmen, wife of the Dictator Franco! I suspect we both guessed that her husband and I were about as far apart politically as it would be possible to be. It added a little piquancy to the situation. The Guardia Civil also realised, smiled, and relaxed.

Another time, I was hitchhiking with a lovely Filipina friend from Madrid to Toledo in order to see Toledo's most important religious procession of the year when the incredible silver monstrance is paraded. The car we were in, driven by a Galician couple also en route to Toledo for the procession, became overheated and started to blow steam. I offered to go and get water from a nearby farmstead while the engine cooled down. The couple insisted we leave them and try immediately for another lift to get to Toledo on time, but I felt honour bound to stay and help them. Just then two Guardia Civil rolled up on motorbikes. After hearing our explanations, they too overruled me and declared that it was imperative that Cora and I got to Toledo without delay. Hitchhiking, incidentally, was illegal in Spain, unless one had obtained a certificate of insurance with one's photograph and ID attached (quite a sensible measure) and then only available to certain categories of people such as conscripts and students. Tactfully overlooking such formalities, the Guardia then summarily stopped the very next car, one hand waving, the other resting on their revolvers in typical Guardia Civil stance. The car proved to be a Rover belonging to a middle-class British couple en route to Portugal via Madrid and Toledo. Then ensued a glorious Bob Newhart-type monologue, conducted by myself as interpreter: "You see - er - these two men with funny hats and revolvers. Well - er - they seem to want you to carry us to Toledo. In fact, they seem to be insisting on it." We got in and were driven off in style to the waves of the Galician couple and the salutes of the smiling Guardia Civil. The British couple remained staring straight ahead, and for some reason appeared tense. After the procession, Cora and I went down to the Tagus. I had my fishing rod with me. I then made the unoriginal discovery that women and fishing don't mix. One can't concentrate fully on two things at once. It was time to move on.

For me, as for many others, Egypt was to prove an overwhelming historical experience. I climbed the Great Pyramid of Cheops (now forbidden), and was taken inside the even older step-pyramid of Djoser and saw the five-thousand year old cedar of Lebanon panelling forming part of the funerary chamber, wonderfully preserved in the dry desert air. I spent time in Luxor visiting the Valley of the Kings etc., spent a very enjoyable afternoon in a chartered dinghy at Aswan cataract, and was suitably impressed by the new Aswan dam a-building. Over the ten-year period of its construction it was to increase the irrigated land of Egypt by one quarter; over the same period the population of Egypt increased by one quarter.

But the real delight was to get away from the tourist trail, fascinating as that may have been, and enjoy life with an excellent Egyptian geological field party in the rock desert during the mild winter months. We climbed Gebel Sikait and from its summit gazed on a wonderful panorama from the desert to the Red Sea. We worked hard and enjoyed our Fridays swimming and basking on beaches of sand and coral on the Red Sea coast. We were not far from the route of the old Roman road that followed sandy wadis through the mountains and linked the Nile near Luxor to the Red Sea at Berenice. One time we took off on a four-wheel-drive safari to do some reconnaissance geology and came across a Roman fort on the line of this road that had been half washed away by occasional flash floods over two millenniums. We navigated by the sun and, on two occasions, by the stars. On several occasions a small yellow wren-like bird came and perched very close to us, once on my shoulder.

There was no rain the whole two and a half months we were in the desert, but some Bedouin managed to survive there with their herds of goats feeding on the occasional thorn scrub, and utilising very rare water pools amid some rocky hollow places in the hills. The physical possessions of these Bedouin were very few, the most prominent being goat-skins of water. I was once moved at the sight of a very recent Bedouin grave – a simple ring of stones, a few pieces of fluttering cloth, a shallow bowl containing water not yet evaporated – all in the clear space, wind, and loneliness of the desert. By contrast, young Bedouin children were buried among the ruins of a deserted city near the emerald mines, where perhaps they were happier in the company and whisperings of numerous departed spirits than in the clean desert wastes that their parents had come to love.

I particularly admired the one Bedouin man, Abaid, in our expedition. Slightly built, tireless, he once walked back alone, unasked, many miles in his own time, retracing our steps of the previous day, and retrieved my compass from where I had very carelessly left it. Sometimes we would come across tiny fragments of emerald, but Abaid would generally say "Mus kwais" (no good). One day, I happened to find a sizable flawless-looking emerald crystal, nearly the size of the top joint of my little finger. It was easily the only one of its size and quality we saw the whole time. I offered it to Abaid, because I knew the Bedouin made money by selling such emeralds on the coast to dhows crossing the Red Sea. I wanted him to have it but he wouldn't take it, saying it was "kwais ketir" – too good! I carefully wrapped it in my handkerchief, but by the end of the day I had somehow lost it. I was sad about that.

For two days we endured a severe sandstorm. After it had abated the blown sand had plastered itself along the base of the wadi walls. That evening I walked out alone by moonlight to the junction of Wadi Sikait and Wadi Gemel and kicked steps up quite steep hard-packed sand to a dry-stone sentry box on the side of the cliff, built probably in the Ptolemaic era to watch for possible runaway slaves from the emerald mines.

Near these old emerald mines in Wadi Sikait an amazing temple had been cut into the solid bedrock of the wadi wall where there was a big mass of soft talc bedrock. The facade was of classical columns. On the lintel was an inscription in Greek. I tried to note it down but some was difficult to decipher. Some months later in Athens at the Anglo-American Archaeological Institute, I was shown a great leather tome, on a page of which the same inscription had been recorded from the field notes of a 19th century explorer. It read, as I recall, somewhat as follows: "I Antonius came here. First I dug for water. Then I built this temple. I dedicate it to Seraphis, Isis, Apollo, and all the other Gods." Smart chap that Antonius. He certainly had his priorities right, water first, and not forgetting to include both Egyptian and Greek deities – and all the others!

Our field work happened to coincide in part with the month of Ramadan. Daytime fasts cut down on the level of physical activity we could sustain, and we all looked forward to the new moon that would signal the end of Ramadan. On the expected evening I climbed a six-hundred foot hill near our camp at sunset to try and get a glimpse of any new moon. But no luck, despite excellent visibility. Later that evening, we heard on the radio that the very slender crescent new-moon had in fact just been sighted at the observatory at Rabat (the furthest west in the Old World, where the moon was just that little more advanced in its path in relation to the sun). We had a good party that night.

I travelled slowly back through the Levant, an area which provided much food for reflection: Mount Sinai and the long Christian tradition of St. Catherine's. Jericho, with its ancient walls and the contemporary misery of Palestinian refugee camps. Jerash, a spectacular Graeco-Roman city in a parched and eroded landscape. Jerusalem, where I lingered. Beirut, a pleasant, sophisticated, and tolerant city then where Muslim, Christian, and Jew lived happily together, now of course devastated beyond belief.

A last visit to Spain and back to England with the offer of a research job with a cement company at Gravesend. At the job interview they noticed my jaw drop when they mentioned two weeks holiday a year – but rising to three after ten years, they offered. But my freedom seemed too much to give up. The melody and words of "Ya se van los pastores" sung by Victoria de Los Angeles still haunted me. I declined. Clearly, I was not the stuff of which British industry was made. But what to do?

I ended up for a while in the Hebrides, vagabonding in lonely places where I had geologised in times past in my student days. I found it overwhelmingly nostalgic. Strange that I had been too busy then to visit Iona, the cradle. Time passed there without reckoning. I meditated in the megalithic monuments of Callanish and elsewhere. I remembered, even in my busy student days, having been fascinated by the wide vistas of landscape and seascape afforded by the Hebrides. I had watched the flight and migrations of the birds, had star-gazed, and had observed the passage of the sun during the waxing days of Spring, using a carpenter's ruler crudely as a sextant. Clearly, these megalith builders had also observed the passage of the seasons, and in a masterly fashion too.

It was during this long wandering visit that I had an amazing chance encounter with an old geological comrade, Nigel Baird, on the little mail boat in Glen Shiel. In all, we only had time for a hour's chat before we went our respective ways. For a short while I was envious of his continuing productive and settled professional life as a geologist, but I realised I was at peace with myself in my wandering. But then I reflected that my life-style was a selfish one, and I should be thinking of what I could offer. Also, there was the mundane question of supporting myself!

* * * * * * *

School

So, like many better men and women before me, and partly for lack of anything else to do, I drifted into schoolteaching. It was quite easy. In those days, one did not need a teaching qualification, just a degree. Never mind mine was in geology, I ended up teaching maths to O-level and General Studies to the Sixth Form at Burford School in the Cotswolds, after walking in to the school on spec the week before. Rather ominously, the teacher I was replacing had departed suddenly with a nervous breakdown.

Burford still called itself a Grammar School, which it had been for centuries, but it had recently become a Comprehensive School. Moreover, it had a farm attached to it and boarded a few lads who were not quite bad enough for Borstal. They were aroused at some unearthly hour in the morning to milk cows. A surprising proportion of the teachers were Welsh. I asked the obvious question. "Why, it's half way between Cardiff and Twickenham, man!", was the answer. Some of the older teachers found it difficult to adjust to a comprehensive-type intake, but they were a good bunch overall.

I can honestly say that my year's schoolteaching was probably the hardest work I have done in my life, but it was thoroughly rewarding and I enjoyed it. I took the view that one didn't have to know anything in order to teach maths, as it is possible to work everything out from first principles. The higher streams accepted this and worked well. The lower streams needed a little encouragement. Once I got a difficult class to do an original written homework, namely to consider what use maths might be to anyone. The answers were amazingly varied – from useful for understanding pools permutations to the beauty of the universe! I made up a presentation, including points from as many of the class as possible, and read it out back to them. You could have heard a pin drop. They were never any trouble after that. A more senior class got to hear about it, and wanted to do the same. I let them, but they didn't do it with the same originality. The fact was that most of the brighter children tended to become docile and to follow the tramlines of convention. I remember 4A were reluctant to accept the extremely simple and elegant Arabic proof of Pythagoras's Theorem because it was not the "proper" Euclidian proof that they had been previously taught. An original child in an A class tended to stick out and often got penalised by teachers. I was reminded of my own schooldays.

On one occasion I remember that one class had done a good homework, and I happened to comment how pleasant it was to mark well-done work. To my surprise, the next and following homeworks were all exceptionally well done and continued to be so. My "ploy" had only worked because it wasn't a ploy – it was an honest chance remark that I had made in the first place. Imitators beware! A class will immediately spot any insincerity in a teacher.

The catchment area of the school embraced a wide range of social classes. Children aged 11 to 13 were unstreamed in their first two years. From then on they were streamed and it was very noticeable how children from good home backgrounds found themselves in the top two streams, while children from disadvantaged homes ended up in the lowest streams. I quickly learnt how overwhelmingly important is home environment. As a corollary to this, I realised also what a catastrophic waste of innate talent there is in Britain's wretchedly class-structured and wealth-structured society.

The fortunate A and B streams enjoyed class sizes of under thirty. By contrast, the G streams, of lowest academic ability, were all in larger classes. 4G, one of my classes, the lowest stream of the school-leaving year (children could leave school at 15 then) was the largest in the school with 42 children.

I thought this was a disgrace, as these children certainly needed the most individual attention – the exact opposite of the A stream children, whom one could more or less leave to purr along like a well-tuned powerful car. I got the impression that many (not all) of the teaching staff took the view that the sooner 4G left the better. I also learnt that 4G had been a factor in the previous teacher's departure, so I had a problem on my hands.

I was saved by two things. I think 4G realised that I had a genuine sympathy for underdogs and rascals and, more significantly, some of the leading lads had just begun to realise that even to get into an apprenticeship they needed a minimum qualification in maths. At least, there was this credible alternative to the dole in those days. "Why don't we get to do homework, like the other streams?" they asked. So I set up a voluntary "express group" within the class, with a programme of work, to be pursued both in class and at home, leading to C.S.E maths. Prestige in 4G was won, for some at least, by being in the group, not by fooling around. But I can't pretend it was easy.

Every day I drove to and from school through two picturesque Cotswold villages, past fields alive with circling lapwings in the winter months, and across the valleys of the Evenlode and Windrush. From many contacts and conversations I became aware, however, of the baseness and evil that existed among the peasantry of this outwardly serene area. Teachers perforce become realists.

Then events took an unexpected turn. One of the sixth-form boys had been accepted for a place on a schoolboy expedition to Iceland. He had never seen a mountain in his life. Over Whit I took him to North Wales where we camped, carried, and cooked. We climbed Y Garn and the Glyders and made a traverse of Snowdon trying not to use paths. The first few alpines were already in bloom. When I got back there was a telegram waiting that had invited me to immediate interview in London for an attractive research cum teaching post in geology at the new and growing university in Newfoundland. I had not solicited this job, nor indeed any geological job. In fact, that year after returning to England I had finally stopped all subscriptions to geology journals and societies and had sold all my geology books. The headmaster had already asked me what were my plans for next year, and in particular whether I had any plans to resume a professional career in geology. I had assured him then that I was coming back to teach after the summer holidays. It was now past the deadline date for putting in resignations. Also, the professor who had sent me the telegram was now back in Newfoundland.

I was not very proud of my decision. It was to go for the Newfoundland job. The pay would be about three times what I was earning as a teacher in England. Acceptance, however, would depend on a postponed interview with the Newfoundland professor who would be in Switzerland later that summer. I burnt my boats by putting in with embarrassment a late resignation (the headmaster was gracious about the matter), and went to Switzerland with the intention of carrying on to vagabond in Greece and the Greek islands if I was unsuccessful. But I got the job. Three weeks later I was in Newfoundland.

I had worked hard at Burford. I still treasure the award of Qualified Teacher status I received on the basis of practical teaching. The work was worthwhile. It involved giving of myself each day to the two hundred or so children I taught in the six or seven classes in my day's rota. I had the pleasure of seeing them make individual progress. I left with an abiding respect for teachers. True, some are more able than others. But they all constitute society's front-line troops in the ongoing war against anarchy in our "civilisation". There's something else about teaching: any teacher worth his or her salt is continually learning just as much as the pupils!

* * * * * * *

Newfoundland

My departure for Newfoundland was not without serious misgivings. I was not at peace with myself over having let down both Burford and my new-found commitment to teaching. I was also apprehensive about being able to pick up the threads of a geological career. I thought I would give things in Newfoundland a year's trial, two years at the most, and then see. I flew into Halifax, Nova Scotia, on a lovely September day, descending over a landscape of forest with scattered diary farms. I felt a sudden tingle of excitement and pride that I was now to be a "landed immigrant" in a spacious and lovely country. Much later that night, I arrived at St. John's, the capital of Newfoundland, on a connecting milk-run flight. Before landing, the plane circled over the the minute city and its lovely harbour nestling among rocky hills. I thought I had seldom seen anywhere so inviting.

I found Newfoundland to be a beautiful and indeed unique northland at the latitude of Paris, with a unique population, one-third Irish and two-thirds west-country English in origin. I felt an immediate affinity with both the place and its people. I was to stay for over twenty years.

Within the first two weeks of my arrival, I happened to find two places which I never ceased to revisit. The first was a lonely coastal walk along a lighthousekeeper's path round two little bays and headlands to a promontory called Ballyhack. Over the years the path became abandoned, due to the installation of a more reliable automatic light, and increasingly difficult to follow. That only added to its attraction. The lonely landwash was of low wooded cliffs with shingle at their feet, littered with green sea-urchin tests and other flotsam. I used to reflect that I too, like all Newfoundlanders in fact, was a piece of flotsam that had washed up on this lonely island. The difference between me and other Newfoundlanders was that I had arrived a little late, that was all.

The second walk was short in length but resumėed in miniature all mountain walks I had ever made. It started as a lane near an old white timber-framed clap-boarded homestead, which later fell into ruin, and proceeded through hay meadows. These too became abandoned and over the years became reforested by pin-cherry, birch, and rowan. Next the lane became a path which led on up through softwoods of spruce and fir, so reminiscent of the Alps. Then the path broke out above the tree-line into tundra with many blueberries and cowberries, and if you knew where to look for them, cranberries as well. When I first went, the homestead was inhabited and I had asked permission to walk up the lane from the elderly couple who lived there. In season, on my return I would leave a can of cranberries on their doorstep. They have passed away now. The final stage of the walk aimed for a rounded rocky summit, rather like a Buddhist stupa in shape. On gaining it, there was a spectacular view of an enormous bay and far hills and islands. From both Ballyhack and the "stupa", there is not much but ocean and ice between one and the north pole.

I found the first Newfoundland winters long and hard. In later years I discovered that the remedy was cross-country ski-ing, so that instead of bemoaning the cold and the shovelling of driveways after each storm one looked forward to freshened trails through the forest.

In my first Spring, which burst forth at last miraculously after the introverting depths of a very long stormy winter, I discovered while geologising a small untracked lake, about seventy miles from St. John's, well stocked with pan-sized trout. The approach to it lay through a tangle of rocky hills covered in early summer with the prolific creamy flowers of cushion plants of that great Scottish rarity *Diapensia lappponica* (so rare that it has never acquired a common name in Britain). It was in truth a wild and lonely place often troubled by wind and mist. The Diapensia was abundant there, certainly not because of a hospitable setting, but because it could endure where other plants could not. There was an air of pathos about it all. It brought back a memory of a time when I had seen three Iceland poppies growing alone in steep scree on an isolated nunatak among the glaciers and snow of Greenland's mountainous east coast. I often returned to share my fishing place alone with a loon calling from a nearby larger lake. That too brought back memories of Greenland. I remembered a lonely fjord there where I had slipped away from expedition colleagues and sat alone and watched a pair of loon from a sloping shelf of rock at the water's edge where eskimo children had played at building kayaks and igloos out of loose stones. That particular settlement of eskimo people had died out in isolation.

Also that Newfoundland Spring I watched the Portuguese White Fleet of sailing ships, their decks piled high with stacked dories, sail in majestic procession through the Narrows to berth and revictual in St. John's before a long summer of lonely fishing with hand-lines on the Grand Banks of Newfoundland. Their arrival in St. John's harbour was indeed the inspiration of Spring. Alas, no more.

Summer brought a chorus of bird song to the forest. For just a few precious weeks the weather was consistently warmer than in Britain but never oppressively hot. I began the first of many travels in the island province – the size of England but with only one-hundredth the population.

One of my favourite places was the island of Fogo, now I understand regarded as the fourth corner of the world by the Flat Earth Society! Indeed, to stand on the curious rocky hill at Fogo's northern tip and look out over a boundless and lonely grey ocean festooned with icebergs even in midsummer is a remarkable experience. Once I camped on Fogo in a grassy hollow at the head of a small bay and found I was sharing the place with a cavorting herd of ponies. In the winter they came into settlements to be housed and fed in return for work hauling logs, but in the summer they enjoyed their freedom.

Another time in Fogo I stayed with a fisherman's family. The son, a great ox of a man with crooked teeth, dressed in ragged sweaters that failed to meet his trousers at the back, told me of how, just a few weeks previously, a huge humpback whale had become ensnared in his nets and done a thousand dollars worth of damage. He had come straight home and taken down one of the rifles, which I had noted hanging up along with fearsome-looking fowling guns in the living room, and returned in his small skiff with the intention of shooting the whale. When he reached the whale he found he couldn't bring himself to shoot it. Instead, he spent the remainder of the day hacking away at his gear, at times with one foot on or even standing on the whale's back, before eventually freeing the mighty animal. The whale had co-operated by lifting a flipper as he worked his way round. The whale and its mate, who had been waiting nearby all the time, kept him company for some time after the release. I well understood the thing he was saying but didn't put into actual words. That day on that lonely ocean he had been near his Creator.

On another favourite offshore island, Random Island, I used to like to listen to tales told by an elderly man of his youth. In the winters they took horses across the ice in the bay to cut and haul trees. In the Spring run-off they operated a small mill to slab the trunks. Then in summer they used to catch and make (sun-dry) fish (cod). He spoke of those times, which you or I might well regard as very hard, as the best of his life. I believed him. I also met there an old man, aged 95, who had first gone down north to the Labrador as a boy of 14 in the summer of 1886, the first of thirty consecutive summers, travelling by schooner and living in a makeshift "room" on the rocky coast catching and making fish. He too regarded those hard years as the best in his life.

The ethnic mix of Newfoundlanders showed in their character. The Irish gave them gaiety, wit, and music. What other community of 100,000 such as St. John's supports so much rep and a full symphony orchestra? The English gave them practical genius and common sense. It occurred to me that same excellent mix, immediately succeeding the Age of Saints, had once given Britain her enduring place in world history.

In addition, all Newfoundlanders perforce had their character moulded by the environment of the island and its uncompromising climate. Self-reliance, courage, and a degree of recklessness in the face of adversity were prominent traits. Within all this, there was also a rich seam of spirituality. I cannot think of any distinct race of white peoples worthy of greater respect than Newfoundlanders.

Ironically, they were the butt of ignorant "Newfie" jokes emanating from mainland Canada (Newfoundland had voted in 1949 narrowly agreeing to let Canada join them; Canadians were never given the right to vote on the proposed union).

Here I might interject my own droll little Newfie tale. One morning I was leading an international party of geologists around outcrops in Conception Bay. The weather was cool, windy, and damp. Some Canadian participants were inclined to believe that this was typical of Newfoundland, and were making some other comments as well. I took an opportunity to reassure the party that Newfoundland had progressed beyond the quaintness of legend, and cheered them up by promising a good lunch stop. When we arrived at the café in the outport of Harbour Main we found a note on the door: "Closed for lunch".

But Newfoundlanders have the last laugh. Nearly all own their own home. Even today, some young couples will build one together. What possible finer start to a marriage? The man will start by cutting timber and hauling it to a mill for slabbing. Even if out of work (as many are), Newfoundlanders receive the same Federal dole as do poor idiots in a Toronto suburb. The difference is that Newfoundlanders can fish, grow vegetables, kill a moose in the Fall, cut fuelwood in the winter, do odd jobs without telling the taxman, and tend to take the sensible view that as far as fisheries regulations are concerned, they and the lobsters and salmon were there before Federal fisheries officers!

I was constantly struck by the way in which many of my Newfoundland students had had to overcome the problems associated with the provision of education and health care in the scattered coastal settlements from where most of them had come. They were a cheerful, tough, and loyal bunch, at home both in the woods and in small boats, mentally alert and possessing a good sense of humour. They made excellent geologists, and for my part I began to feel reassured that I had something to contribute to them after all, perhaps as much as a better-qualified academic might have done, albeit in different ways.

The university treated me well. Newfoundland became for me a world, a microcosm yes, but a world. From my office window I could watch an osprey fishing, hear the call of the shy sora, or glimpse a bittern among the reeds of the adjacent lake. I was happy. Although never as abrupt an experience as Africa, Newfoundland shaped me while letting me grow. Why ever leave? I sometimes still ask myself this question. But there were reasons. Newfoundland has a poignant history and one was certainly never far from Nature there, but another land with an even longer history was calling me, ever more insistently. Also, one changes, or perhaps, better said, one's perception of one's psyche matures.

At least, I can look back with gratitude on the privilege of having lived in that most beautiful island of Newfoundland and among its fine people for a considerable proportion of my life.

* * * * * * *

A finite world

My early years in Newfoundland happened to witness a great revolution in the way geologists looked at Earth. Our familiar continents and oceans were seen to be merely the transient reflections of "plate tectonics". By great good luck it transpired that Newfoundland was to become an early testing ground of this new synthesis of ideas. It was all fascinating and very exciting. Volcanic activity in particular was to become much better understood in terms of the new paradigm. I was to write a book about this.

What, in retrospect, I find quite interesting about it all was the varied reactions of my fellow geologists. "Conservatives" ignored or even ridiculed the prospect of change. "Revolutionaries" welcomed it. But the flood tide broke all barriers, and within the one year of 1969 virtually all geologists had jumped on the new bandwagon. Plate tectonics is in fact a more sophisticated version of the controversial older notion of "continental drift" that I had always found appealing. I was glad to see the vindication of the work of former geologists of vision such as Alexander Du Toit and Arthur Holmes and particularly that great man Alfred Wegener.

When my turn for a sabbatical year came up after seven years I opted therefore for a round-the-world trip in order to visit, first-hand, "plate boundaries" and related phenomena in such places as Iceland, the Himalayas, Indonesia, New Zealand, Hawaii, and Japan. The President gave me an open round-the-world ticket and I left St. John's with a small rucksack and a small grip, some strong and washable cotton clothing, and I didn't come back for thirteen months. I managed to achieve much of what I had set out to do, but the trip, echoing my vagabond tendencies, had other unforeseen consequences.

Newfoundland, my microcosm and nirvana, had its problems, wryly recognised by the rest of Canada. Essentially, Newfoundland's increasing population, together with rising aspirations, met and exceeded the barrier imposed by the finite limit of Newfoundland's natural resources (the basis of true wealth). There had ensued a recent desperate history of harebrained industrialisation mostly ending in breathtaking failures accompanied by scandal, followed by irresponsible government borrowing just to make ends meet. This was followed by the once-unimaginable complete collapse of the cod fishery (Newfoundland's raison-d'être), due mainly to overfishing by foreign vessels. But why worry. This was just Newfoundland. Either Canada would back the debt, or the Province would go bankrupt as it had done twice before. In any event, bailiffs wouldn't be able to cart away hospitals, harbours, roads, and the new university, and some people would still be foolish enough to lend the Province more money in the future.

The sabbatical year opened my eyes. There is something very salutary about going round the world and keeping one's eyes open. One comes to realise what one should have already known, namely that Earth *is* finite.

It was about this time that the first stunning pictures of Earth from space had first been published, and I came across the following quotation:

> To see the earth as it truly is, small and blue and beautiful in that eternal silence where it floats, is to see ourselves as riders on the earth together, brothers on that bright loveliness in the eternal cold – brothers who know now that they are truly brothers.
>
> Archibald Macleish

It has been claimed that over half of astronauts – not, one would think, a breed likely to indulge in mawkish sentimentality – have told in fact of being profoundly affected by something akin to a religious conversion as a result of their privileged vision of Earth in space.

It was brought home to me during my sabbatical that everywhere on our planet Earth there were problems. The same equation:

Population + Man's Proclivities + Natural Resources + Environment = Future

governs us all. Naturally, the dimensions of the terms on the left-hand side of the equation differ enormously from country to country. But Newfoundland was certainly not alone in being in trouble. We all were.

For example, I witnessed unforgettable scenes of human debasement in an urban setting in Calcutta and of environmental decay in a rural setting in Nepal. Both seemed more distressing than anything I had silently witnessed in Africa years before.

Once I stood on the long swaying suspension footbridge over a tributary of the Baghmati River on the western outskirts of Katmandu, listening to the temple bells. I watched the run-off from the early monsoon rains flooding and filling the wide flat river bed below me. The water looked like reddish-brown soup. This was because it was carrying in suspension enormous quantities of precious topsoil. Later, I travelled up-country from Katmandu and saw why. Population pressure had led to forest clearing and the construction of new terraced fields, clinging one above another to thousands of feet of hillside. Above the fields the steep mountain slopes were heavily tracked by grazing animals, and villagers were cutting and gathering wood for fuel. Forest cover had been reduced to the point where it was now failing to brake the runoff of the annual monsoon rains. Every here and there a wide slash on a hillside filled with rubble and debris, sometimes exposing bedrock, revealed where a recent landslide had taken away the fruits of all the patient work, terraces, topsoil, and all.

The Baghmati is itself just one of the numerous tributaries of the mighty Ganges. For over four decades now the Gangetic Plain of Northern India, the home of over 400 million people, has been subject to unprecedented annual flooding. Each year, around October, our TV screens repeat the story. The floods have been worst in Bangladesh, the country of the joint deltas of the Ganges and Brahmaputra, the greatest delta in the world and the densely populated home of over 100 million people. Between wet seasons some of the vast load of silt settles out from the flood waters of the Ganges, of which the dry-season flow is correspondingly reduced making sections of the river now unnavigable. At the mouths of the delta yet more silt is adding to the area of large low-lying islands. Their fertility encourages settlement and agriculture, although these islands are well known to be prone to devastating and deadly flooding by storm surges.

The full extent of this whole ecological debacle, of which I saw a tiny fraction but came to understand, almost defied comprehension. It is now very seriously affecting the lives of 10% of the world's population.

The above is noteworthy because of its vast scale. But precisely the same deadly cycle of deforestation and erosion affects Ethiopia, Kenya, north-east Brazil, Madagascar, the Philippines, and a great many other places.

In less wet areas the phenomenon of spreading desertification, also associated with deforestation, affects the lives of 700 million more people, again with desperate consequences, notably in the African Sahel.

Destitute landless peasants swell the ranks of the world's cities. Even their appalling living standards there are better than the utter misery that they have left behind, but the urban slums merely provide a reservoir of concentrated hopelessness and disease. The divorce of peasants from their land is actually increased by the penetration of our money economy and of the much-heralded "Green Revolution" (heavily predicated on access to capital for seed, fertilizers, pesticides, machinery, and irrigation).

To cap it all, it became apparent to me that much of the affluence that some of us enjoy is predicated on the completely unsustainable exploitation of a bonanza of coal and oil that will just not last and cannot, of course, be replaced.

Some of this was impinging on my consciousness during my year's travel. Much more I was to document later. On one occasion, I tentatively mentioned some of my growing concerns to the Director of the New Zealand Geological Survey. He successfully contrived to convey the impression that I was an ignorant, doom-watching, communist, useless, Pommie bastard without, I recall, actually using any of those words. Later, I gave an invited lecture to the Geological Society of Australia in Canberra. I chose as my theme "The geologist, exploiter or conserver?" It went down quite well, once people had got over the shock of a non-technical talk. Halfway through an animated discussion time, one person created a bit of a stir when he got up and stalked out. It turned out to be the Director of the Geological Survey who, I was later told, was facing the sack by the new incoming government for being too much of a heedless exploiter in mining policies and not enough of a conserver!

It was in conversations with Minao Minato, the doyen of Japanese geology, that I found a like mind. Minao, a quiet and gentle man, had been in charge of managing the exploitation of minerals and oil in Malaysia and Indonesia following their rapid overrunning by Japanese forces early in the war. Perhaps, if my visit had been a decade or two earlier, when painful memories of the war were fresher, I might have found it difficult to talk to him. But memories of the war had now receded. Minao had done much of his early work long before the war in the remote Kuril Islands, sailing there in a small five-ton boat, and we found that we had "northern" experiences in common. He now chose to live in Hokkaido, the northernmost island, the "Newfoundland" of Japan. Indeed, there were some striking similarities of climate and attitudes between the two.

Unlike most of his colleagues who had modern homes, Minao lived with his wife and charming daughter in a traditional log cabin. This was very comfortable with a central wood stove. I enjoyed several meals there. In his office, Minao used to brew up tea using the same small kerosene stove (like a miniature primus stove) that he had had with him in the Kurils. We went out into the field together a couple of times, but mostly we just talked at our leisure. Yes, this industrial civilisation with all that it entails must end, we agreed. Then, essentially, it will be back to the land. But how, for example, can the land of Japan support 120 million Japanese? Minao shrugged his shoulders. He knew the answer, or at least the terms in which an answer will perforce be addressed. It just so happened that during the time we were together a shiver ran through the industrial world when OPEC action effectively quadrupled the price of oil.

Back in Newfoundland, I started to collaborate with another radical geologist in an off-beat course called "Geology in the Service of Man". Before long I found I had the course to myself and renamed and divided it into two: "Natural Resources and the Past" and, more ominously, "Natural Resources and the Future".

Terms such as greenhouse effect, acid rain, ozone layer, etc. are rather boring clichés now, but they were novel then. Besides the many interesting scientific aspects of environmental science, I found that to get students to fully understand and think about the equation mentioned above, it was necessary to encourage an increasingly wide-ranging approach. The courses came to include discussion of such things as reasons for the rise and fall of past civilisations (mostly to do with abuse of topsoil), the unique nature of contemporary world capitalism, a seeking in contemporary religions for ethical bases appropriate to a post-industrial society, and so on. Some conservative colleagues were horrified. They considered my courses subversive and petitioned the Dean to have then stopped. Even my Head of Department was nervous about antagonising corporations, some of whom provided us with financial support. Fortunately the Dean took the view that if my courses were having the effect of making geologists and others think, they might inherently be not a bad thing!

I became immersed in a lot of new reading and ideas, and dropped out of conventional geological research. One fateful day I received two items of mail by the same post. One was an advance copy of my geological book that I mentioned above. The second was an advice that my geological research grant was to stop because of my lack of productivity of profess-ional research papers (a serious matter for an academic). I took both items to the President, who was a historian by profession. I want to teach the history of the future, I told him, rather grandiosely. Yes, he nodded gravely, some university history departments do indeed include that. I also mentioned that I had just heard that there was going to be a new Canadian granting agency called HCST (Human Context of Science and Technology) and that I intended to apply for support, if only to give myself some acad-emic credibility. It was nice, I added, to see Ottawa doing something intelligent and unconventional for a change. Just as I was leaving, the President confided with a smile that he had been the chairman of a comm-ittee that had just considered and recommended this very development! He smiled at my obvious genuine embarrassment. I got my grant. Several Humanities professors who thought that they should have been funded received nothing.

I enjoyed my "subversive" courses. I couldn't preach at my students or indoctrinate them, but I could encourage them to widen their horizons and think for themselves about matters of vital importance. Some students were puzzled by nominally science courses that did not require them to regurg-itate facts, but rather to present reasoned arguments of their own, even disagree with the lecturer, and thus contribute to their own and their class-mates' personal development and understanding. I think the courses succ-eeded with some, perhaps most, of their participants. Once, I remember a good student who was very quiet in manner suddenly standing up in class and declaring, "Yes, what *are* we here for?" (the vital question), and just as suddenly sitting down again, looking somewhat surprised at himself. He meant, I hope, what were we doing on planet Earth, not in my class!

I tried to gather my new-found concerns into another book, "Mother Earth and the Future of Humanity". It was never published. It was too green by far for the conventional academic scientific press, and perhaps too scientific for the numerous fringe green publishers that were beginning to sprout up. Looking at the manuscript again, I realise that it was also too long and indigestible. It represented an uncomfortable revolt of my psyche against the narrownesses of geology, science, academia, and conventional wisdoms.

I continued to enjoy my natural-resource courses, while continuing to teach conventional first and second year courses in geology. My position, although open to attack by some, was readily defensible. I felt I was doing a good job and I enjoyed breaking new ground. I also made several new friends who shared cross-disciplinary interests. Although I was no longer doing research purely in geology, I felt that I was pulling my weight in our department, where I enjoyed the confidence of our excellent new Head.

Then events overtook me again.

* * * * * * *

Dreamtime and farewell

In the summer of 1988 I found myself rather alone in St. John's handling two first-year geology courses in the university's newly opened summer semester. It was an excellent time for teaching first-year students and for pleasant field excursions with them – far better than trying to rush to cram field trips into the Fall term before the winter weather closed in with yet untrained novice classes. The courses were easy to teach as enrolments were fairly light and I enjoyed the students and our outings. I was care-taking the house of a friend who, like most of my geological colleagues, was away in the field. I had the place to myself. It overlooked the city, dramatically so at night, but was very quiet. After a leisurely meal I would go for solitary evening walks in the woods and hills that surround the city. One of my recreations that summer was making a diary of the dates of flowering of wild flowers and of the flowers in the university botanical garden. I spent a lot of time taping some of my friend's excellent classical CD collection. I also became very interested in Jung and his work. All in all, it was a very peaceful time.

I found myself dreaming a lot and, for the first time in my life, I decided to make a conscious effort to record the dreams in writing immed-iately on waking. With discipline and without other distractions I found that this was remarkably easy to do. In fact, as soon as I concentrated, the dream descriptions seemed to write themselves very readily. I quickly realised that the dreams meant something and were important.

In all, I had over thirty major dreams that summer. When I looked over my notes, it was obvious that they fell into several well-defined groups as follows:

1. End of my geology days.
2. Desire for a more contemplative and spiritual life.
3. Impatience with, and overthrow of, a conventional person (persona?)
4. Uneasiness about the future of our "civilisation".
5. The "Hamlet" syndrome – to take up arms or not?
6. Return to Celtic lands.

Just as these topics interlock, so did many of the dreams. Here, concisely, are a few examples:

A. I was cutting out a picture from a newspaper for a scrapbook. The picture was of a group of geologists, including a back view of myself (complete with distinctive tonsure!), looking at a remarkably complicated but surrealistic outcrop; i.e., my geological days were over and a fit subject for a scrapbook! In passing, I marvelled that my subconscious had enough "bytes" to be able to fabricate such a complicated fictional geological structure.

B. I was following a clear surveyed line marked with raised surveyor's cord and flagstones. I even extended the line using a compass. Then a field trip of geologists took off to go even further. They wanted me to come with them. But I had seen a cinema. The time of showing of the main film conflicted with the field trip. The film was in Italian. I wondered if I would be able to understand a novel language. Some sympathetic bystanders assured me that I would. So I decided to go to the cinema and watched my geological friends go off in a land-rover.

C. I was walking along a crowded sidewalk with a woman friend while an impatient fellow behind, dressed in a blue suit, was pushing and shoving me. I let him go on and kicked his shins. The woman asked why had I given way? I replied he's better out of the way and anyway I gave him a good kick in passing. The woman and I then went and browsed leisurely in a bookstore with a kind Indian storekeeper.

D. I was in a house and looking through an half-open door into a bare room containing a closed roll-top desk illuminated in the sun's rays. I knew that there was something of extreme importance to be revealed in the desk. But before I could do anything I knew I had to kill the other person in the house. That person, dressed in a blue suit was, incredibly, Nigel Baird. I killed him because I knew that if I didn't he would only kill me. I found this distressing as I had nothing whatever against Nigel.

E. I was on a beach and knew there was a tidal wave coming, but I couldn't persuade others to move to a safer position. I had several variants of this dream.

F. A curious construct of a dream of me looking at myself in a dream; i.e. looking at a story in which I was one of the participants. It was of trench warfare and I knew I was going to die in the war. I was an officer and had a comfortable room with a grate and a fire. Why go out on sallies? They were dangerous and pointless – or *were* they pointless if I was going to die anyway?!

G. I was at Euston station trying to find times of trains to Ruabon from the station master. We were interrupted by an impatient man in a blue suit who wanted to travel to somewhere direct on straight lines. The station master brusquely gave him directions and then turned kindly to me. He said that although I had missed the best train, I could still get to Ruabon if I followed his advice and took a slow train to Chester and changed. Why Ruabon, I asked myself. Ruabon is an inconsequential place which has given its name to a particularly monotonous kind of red brick. It was not until the following day

> that the penny dropped. Ruabon was a junction I had often passed in my childhood on trains from Merseyside to Oswestry. It was the junction for the old line that led westwards through a medley of lovely places up the Dee Valley and across the mountains to the Welsh coast. It was the route of my first cycling exploration of North Wales,

The dreams reinforced each other and I became quite certain of their meanings and significance. I accepted them. I began to feel that my subconscious psyche was working with me, powerfully. It was a feeling of enormous elation.

I cannot recommend those books which allegedly interpret dreams, based on an array of symbols. That, it seems to me, is largely rubbish. Dreams are personal. They are, in fact, the only way one's psyche can talk to one. It does so in dream-messages that are, or should be, interpretable to the dreamer alone (*not* by someone else), because they relate to one's own personal experiences. They may, or may not, include archetypal figures like Jung's Wayshower (my kind station master and Indian bookstore keeper) or Shadow (poor old Nigel). I would guess that in periods when one is not in sync with one's psyche one dreams more. That is to say one's psyche is desperate to communicate. So, I believe, it was with me.

I realised also that dreams are like geology. One is presented with multivariant scenarios in both, representing experiments done by Nature and visual messages from the psyche respectively. The art (science?) lies in the experience of interpretation.

Now admittedly my dreams were not far removed from some of my conscious thoughts and reasoning at that time. But I would not have come as quickly to the same conclusion without the aid of dreams. Their message was loud and clear. I resigned, and took a very early retirement.

I have never regretted this. It was time, as Joseph Campbell would say, to "follow one's bliss" and I needs must, as Colman said many centuries ago:

> Return to the land whose love gives you no rest.

My spirits and centuries of history were calling me back to the Celtic fringe of Europe, particularly to Wales and Ireland.

> . . . his heart belonged to the lonely places,
> To a weathered people with ancient faces.
>
> Margaret Gillies Brown

As a geological swansong, I wrote an article for the Canadian geological magazine about how geologists should be in the forefront of facing the contemporary challenges posed by our declining "civilisation". They could and should apply various facets of their geological expertise and experience to current affairs and the future of *Homo sapiens* on Earth.

I was astonished by the response to this article. A large number of geologists from many countries wrote expressing their agreement and support, many of them with comments to the effect that my article had precisely echoed their own previously unvoiced concerns.

In St. John's, some of my colleagues agreed privately that it was important that at least some geologists were prepared to speak out on these matters. Several asked me not to quote them as they didn't want their academic position to be prejudiced! Some of my more conservative colleagues (who would probably not agree with my premises) studiously ignored my article and, in addition, were probably quite glad to see the back of me. Frankly, I couldn't now have cared for their opinions, excellent scientists and people though they may have been.

> How many learned men are working at the forge of science – laborious, ardent, tireless Cyclopes, but one-eyed!
>
> Joseph Joubert

There was also a poignant sense of déjà vu. I seemed to be repeating the experience of a "defining moment" and then leaving a familiar circle of friends and colleagues for new and unknown experiences, often in lonelier circumstances.

Naturally, after a score of years, some links were hard to break. I returned to Newfoundland for two successive summers, not to work or teach, but just to quietly live and follow my bent without pressures. I went out by boat to be among the whales and sea-bird colonies, and walked on the barrens with the island's caribou herd. I made a 1500 mile return journey to spend some time at the only known Viking site in North America. I revisited my fishing pond, favourite walks, and Fogo Island. I made a long last relaxing trip by coastal boat to settlements which still had no road access. I spent some time on the river which the Beothuck Indians (now extinct) had used to travel from their winter camps deep in the shelter of the forest to the coast where they fished and gathered shellfish in the summer. I found that some friendships became deeper and more precious while others faded with the prospect of leaving. I found also that many friends quickly responded to my talking honestly of my new feelings and evolving objectives. Had I lived in a kind of strait-jacket before? Perhaps many of us do for much of our lives!

And of course, some of my own spirit remained. M, will you remember me and think of my spirit:

When the September harvest moon rises above the Southside Hills?

When, at dawn in early October, the brown trout in profusion are leaping the waterfall in Rennies Mill River?
When, on a calm sunny morning later in October, the hill behind Long Pond is aflame with birch, cherry, and maple, all reflected in the still water beneath a clear blue sky?
When, in early November, the brown trout are spawning in the incredibly small brook that flows out of Kent's Pond?
When the first dwys of snow caress the windswept city (a foretaste of winter horrors to come, alleviated by having a strong Newfoundland woman by one's side!)?
When every community of painted timber houses is lit with Christmas lights reflected in the snow?
When, in early evening in mid January, brightest Sirius rises directly right above the harbour Narrows and changes from pink to green to silver (prompting phone-calls to CBC about an UFO!)?
When you are the first on ski-trails freshened with overnight snow still heavy on the branches?
When the March sun begins to feel warm and one can look out in comfort over the city from the top of Nagle's Hill while skiing in the open?
When the river starts to make inroads into the ice at the head of Long Pond and black duck can be seen, along with pintail and teal?
When, in mid April, the fox-sparrow is first heard, and then seen too on the big tree near the bridge at Kent's Pond?
When you repeat the walk up to Prince's Lookout with the bonus in late April of the view of skeins of pack-ice drifting into the great blue expanse of Conception Bay?
When, for a few magic days at the end of May, the head of Long Pond is pure white with acres of flowering bogbean, echoed by the subtler whites of the pin-cherry blossom on the hillside behind, and the first brood of black ducklings are already dabbling?
When you go fishing in that secret lake in May and listen again to the cry of the loon?
When the woods become alive with birdsong throughout June?
When in early July the ox-eye daises begin to flower and remind one of true friends and of our mortal span on this lovely planet?
When in high summer one can lie in peace on a cliff-top in the dry heather with a loved one and watch the ocean, or go swimming in the ponds on the Three Pond Barrens?

Will you remember – and understand – and forgive??

So now all my Newfoundland friends remain ever young in my memory. Like the fallen, "they shall not grow old, nor the years condemn", and they will continue to remain eternally young in my own Tir nan Og across the western sea.

The drover

You might well suppose that an Intercity train is an unlikely place for a small drama. But let me tell you what I witnessed in one, late one afternoon that February following my final return from Newfoundland, all within the space of about twenty minutes, while speeding across the Cheshire plain north-westward from Crewe.

It had been a stormy few days, and the first break in the clouds for some time came in the west as that evening approached. The setting sun underlit an undulating cloud layer with shades of crimson and purple. Below it were numerous wisps and scud of flying cloudlets lit up in orange and red. Far away, close to the western horizon, the sky was completely clear and bright vermilion in colour. It was an extraordinary sight. The whole western sky was ablaze. If a painter could have captured it on canvas, he would not have been believed. Furthermore, the patterns of vivid colour were continuously changing. The crowded coach of some sixty people became virtually silent as we all watched a skyscape that I have seldom, if ever, seen equalled.

Just shielding the low setting sun itself from our direct view was a range of mountains silhouetted in jet black. A lady next to me opined that it must be Snowdon. How English people do tend to equate any prominent Welsh mountain with Snowdon! Maybe I should just have kept my mouth shut, but then there would not have been a story. And anyway I knew these mountains. They were in fact the little-known range known as the Berwyns, looking very grand on this occasion. Surprisingly high, they lie to the west of my father's home near Oswestry, which owes its sunny climate to their shelter. I had once been told that my drover ancestors, many generations back, had driven Welsh sheep and the hardy Welsh Black cattle over these mountains, though I had been told little else about them. So I told the lady the mountains' proper name. I mentioned also that so unfrequented were they that one of the highest summits had only recently acquired its own name, proposed by a group of hikers, Craig Uchaf, a name that has been officially adopted by the Ordnance Survey and now appears on their maps.

It was at that moment that I became uncomfortably aware of a glare from a gentleman across the aisle. Yes, he said, but for every one fancy hiker that may wander along those mountains, a thousand men and ten thousand beasts had travelled across them in years past. I realised at once that he must be referring to the great droving routes, themselves following routes taken by Celtic Saints, Roman soldiers, Bronze Age axe traders, and Neolithic farmers in the thousands of years before them. He raised an arm and pointed to the mountains as he rose to his feet – a tall, craggy man, unmistakably North Welsh in appearance and speech. Yes, he repeated, I can tell you a true story of this.

His story mentioned Llanarmon, so I guessed he was talking of the drover's route that crosses the Berwyns to there from Llandrillo. Even today, the route is still traceable. It is marked by a wide grassy sward winding across the hills among the heather and bracken. At the highest point on the pass, looking westwards at some 1750 feet above sea level, you will see a wonderful panorama of the far peaks of Snowdonia.

The drovers who once used this route and other now-disused routes across the mountains were, for the most part, highly respected men. Leaving their families behind, they undertook the responsibility and hardship of long arduous journeys. The livelihoods of the stock farmers of North Wales depended entirely upon the skill, acumen, and honesty of these drovers. The droving business helped lead to the development of banking in this country. One could say much more of the drovers, but let us hear the craggy Welshman's story, of which I will do my best to remember the details.

Late one summer two centuries ago, he related, a well-known drover and his men were leading large flocks of sheep together with some Welsh Black cattle from Gwynedd en route to fattening pastures in Aylesbury, prior to their sale for slaughter in London. The several men and their dogs had been joined at Bala by other travellers, as was not unusual for reasons of company and safety. These included a tinker with his packhorse, a mounted cleric, and two students and a fiddler on foot.

But the oddest character was a wild woman of uncertain age carrying on her bent back a load of coarse knitted stockings, probably to sell in Shrewsbury, where she might also have been seeking domestic service. Black was her hair, save where it was flecked with grey. Black were her eyes, save one which was flecked with cataract. Black was her dress, save where it was flecked with dirt and grey mould. Barefoot she walked and curtly she declined the drover's kindly offer of a beast to help with her burden.

With mounting excitement I recognised the characteristic cadences, the threefold patterns, and other tricks of narration of the traditional Welsh storyteller, of whom few alas remain, and I have tried to reproduce his patterns of speech where I can remember them.

Wild she looked and wild she was, continued our narrator. She spoke little, only enough that they knew she was from a remote cottage in a certain wild and secret valley. Guarded by dark marshes is that valley, and overlooked by a great black cliff, the only place where black cormorants are known to breed inland. In that same valley stand the ruins of a stronghold of the Princes of Gwynedd, the last to be discovered and conquered by the murderous Edward. Narrow and rocky and impassable is part of that valley, overgrown with alder, ash, and wych elm. Above this narrow place in the valley stood a miserably poor shepherd's house, reached only across the moors, and it was there whence she came. The thought of that dreadful remote place made hardened men shudder.

The motley party successfully crossed the high Berwyn that day, the most demanding stage of all their long droving journey. Our drover had got the caravan moving at earliest dawn, one of the secrets of good droving. Their pace up to the pass had been a calm and steady two miles an hour or so, the sheep content to follow the lean black cattle, the beasts responding to the drovers' continual cries of "Hipe-tra-hooo", an age-old cry already ancient before language was ever written down.

At the lonely pass, each person paused briefly and looked back on a panorama vouchsafed to few – an improbable tangle of the high mountains of the Arans, Rhinogs, Yr Wyddfa, Glyders, and the Carneddau. Only the wild woman never paused to look back on mountains she was destined never to see again.

On the descent the beasts were left to go virtually at their own pace, their tiredness, hunger, and desire to graze being more than matched by their eagerness to reach the richer pastures further down the valley. So they had all reached Llanarmon safely that evening as a full moon rose. That night they relaxed in the drovers' inn which is now a quiet weekend place for "English" people [our story-teller actually used with barely concealed contempt the word Saesneg]. But in those days the inn was alive. "Gwair tymherus porfa flasus, cwrw da cwal cysurus" – worthwhile grass and pleasant pasture, good beer and comfortable shelter, he translated for us [It is in fact a traditional motto that you can still see painted in Welsh on a drovers' inn as far away as Stockbridge in Hampshire on a Welsh droving route].

The drover had seen that the beasts were properly settled and watered, and that the dogs were fed. The traditional arrangement was made with the innkeeper to feed the drovers' dogs on their return journey. For the dogs would be sent back home alone from Buckinghamshire; they would follow without fail the same route back to Gwynedd, and rest at the same inns where they had stayed on their long outward journey. After a good meal, there was fiddling, singing to the harp, storytelling, and wrestling. Everyone was relaxed and cheerful. Our drover had even gone a friendly round with the local champion of the Ceiriog valley and, after a drink or two or more, was feeling very pleased with the day and with himself when he went to bed. Where the wild woman slept nobody knew or cared, only that it was outside somewhere with the beasts, even though the night had become stormy. She had not joined the company in the inn.

In the early hours the drover found himself awake. The wind was moaning continuously in the eaves of the inn. He thought he had heard a terrible scream, but didn't know if he had dreamt it or not. Then he became aware that the beasts were restless. The responsibility for them of course never left his shoulders. Still half asleep, he pulled on his cloak and went out. The cattle were unquiet, the dogs were whining, and the sheep seemed very nervous. Investigating further, in intermittent light as clouds raced across the face of the moon, suddenly he glimpsed a sight in the upper fold which terrified him and for a long moment held him spellbound. On the back of one of the sheep was a large black animal with black eyes flecked with white that stared unblinkingly at him. Its fangs and mouth were red with gore. Instinctively, the drover drew his knife and killed it. Then, still half asleep, and still half wondering if he were dreaming, he had staggered back to his bed.

They found her next day in the early morning in the upper fold, the wild woman, the blood already turning black from the terrible wound where the drover's knife, still in her chest, had killed her. They found the drover too, still with some blood on his cloak and hands. No one knew why, and he couldn't explain why, he had killed her. His story was bizarre and quite unbelievable. The drover was a respected man, but murder is murder. So they hanged him next to the inn. Justice was simple and direct in the valleys in the days before the English came with their police and other curious ways.

That might be the end of it, but they say that you can still hear a body thumping against the side of the inn on a stormy night – well, that could just be the inn sign or something else working loose in the wind. They also say that you can sometimes at night hear a blood-curdling shriek – well, city visitors may not be used to screech-owls calling. But they do say, however, that sometimes, after a wild stormy night, a sheep is found mauled and dead with curious neck wounds, unlike those made by a dog, wounds which no one can explain. They also say that for many years now people swear they have caught glimpses of a large black animal, described as a puma-like creature, in these very hills.

The storyteller looked round the coach. Everyone was silent, one could almost say embarrassed, as English people tend to become when anything out of the ordinary happens. Indeed, no one had stirred since he began his extraordinary tale. He had spoken like a man possessed and we had all felt his strange power. The western sky, still a dull red, was now fading into darkness, and the smooth Intercity train was slowing. I wished I had asked him his name and whence he came, but just before he made to get off at Chester, presumably to connect with local transport for North Wales, I found myself instead impelled to ask him if he happened to know the name of the drover, the subject of his terrible story. Looking me straight in the eyes, the name he unhesitatingly gave me was my own! I was left speechless. With a jolt I suddenly realised I was "home".

* * * * * * *

City of the Legions

Following my return, several times I walked the walls of Chester and gazed over to Wales. I followed the same route from Chester to the Dee that Edward I had taken seven centuries ago past the ruined castle and Norman church of Shotwick. In times of peace, this was a trading route along which packhorses carried Cheshire salt to Wales, but in 1277 it was described as "The Kynge's highway near Chester for our Lord the Kynge to leide his host in the time of warre unto Shotwick ford." I looked again at the hollows on the stones of Shotwick church porch where Edward's archers had sharpened their arrows before they set their faces to the west wind and to Wales. I talked with the fishermen netting salmon on the Dee as they have done for centuries. I gazed again on Edward's castles around the coast of North Wales, incomparable land of legend, of mountains and beaches, saints and scholars. Southwest of Chester I attended again the fair and sheepdog trials in the Welsh valley where my father had been born, all little changed in nearly a century.

I also roamed again familiar countryside between Dee and Mersey with its signs of occupation by man since Mesolithic times. I was appalled to witness the paucity of ships in the Mersey and the loss of a seagoing tradition among the men of Wirral, coupled with the loss of much of the ancillary industry and services of a once great port. Chronic unemployment and the lack of hope among young people were causing many to turn to drugs and crime. I roamed again beaches washed by the Celtic Sea where as a boy I had raked cockles, and there too I was immensely saddened to realise that these lovely shores will remain irretrievably polluted for millenniums to come by radioactive waste discharged from Sellafield.

But there were still the birds, each one playing its individual part in the miracle of the great rhythms of annual migrations of millions along the Atlantic-Celtic flyway. For two brief magical periods each year those that fly south to winter on the Dee from breeding grounds I had visited in the Arctic overlap with summer visitors that fly north from the Africa that I once knew so well.

Frequently, however, I found myself drawn to revisit Chester, where I had often cycled nearly half a century previously. Chester stands proudly at the neck of the Wirral peninsula and is built of a unique mixture of warm red sandstone, half-timbering, and Georgian brick. No other place in Britain, with the exception of Edward's small bastide towns of Conwy and Caernarfon, has its medieval walls quite so complete, still standing for much of their length on their Roman foundations.

Unlike Lancaster, Manchester, Gloucester, and a great many more, all of them Roman sites, the name Chester is unqualified, as it is in Welsh also – quite simply "Caer", the fortress. It is indeed a rather special place, recognised by its status as a European Heritage City.

It was here on low red sandstone bluffs overlooking a broad loop of the River Dee that the Romans constructed the largest of their three great British legionary fortresses. They christened their fortress city with the ancient Celtic name of Deva. They built it well. The four principal streets of Deva in the form of a cross remain the main streets of the centre of Chester today, just as they were when Daniel Defoe described them as "the best ornament of the city, very broad and fair, and run through the whole city in strait lines, crossing in the middle".

For three centuries Deva was home to Roman legions, first the pioneering 2nd Legion, and later for some 200 years the illustrious 20th Valeria Victrix Legion that had campaigned so brilliantly in the conquest of north and west Britain under the personal command of Agricola in A.D.80 to A.D.84. Abruptly, around A.D.370, the remaining legionnaires left.

And for over three centuries the city inside its massive walls of red sandstone apparently remained only barely or intermittently inhabited. Out of the mists of history Nennius records that Arthur himself once fought a battle here. And for ten generations people must have spoken wonderingly of the lonely city of the north-west whose name was passed down by word of mouth quite simply as the City of the Legions.

Then, some thirteen centuries ago in A.D.689 the Saxon King Ethelred founded a small church just without the walls of the deserted city on the site, so the legend goes, where he had seen a white hind in the forest.

In the early 10th century Aethelflaeda, "Queen of the Mercians", daughter of King Alfred the Great, re-occupied the city and extended the walls of the rectangular Roman fortress westwards and southwards to their present line. With Chester as a base, Aethelstan, grandson of King Alfred, decisively defeated a combined army of Danes, Irish, and Scots nearby at the

Battle of Brunaburgh in A.D.937, reputedly the bloodiest battle ever fought on British soil.

In A.D.972 King Edgar the Peaceful, immediately following his coronation at Bath, came to the thriving city of Chester, now housing a royal mint, and was rowed by eight British tribal chieftains up the River Dee to the site of Ethelred's church and received their fealty there. History does not tell us whether the eight British chieftains who obliged with the oars laboured against Dee's ebb tide or had a comparatively easy time on the flood!

After the successful invasion of England by the Normans in 1066, Chester held out longer than any other English city but eventually fell in 1070. The following year William the Conqueror created his nephew Hugh Lupus the first Earl of Chester and swordbearer of England. This was a matter of consequence, as the great sword, which now rests in the Tower of London, gave its rightful owner the duty to restrain the king himself should he exceed his powers.

Hugh Lupus, as did many other Norman barons, acted quickly to consolidate his position and began building on a scale that Chester had not seen since Roman times. In A.D.1075 the construction began of a cathedral over the foundations of the old Saxon church. Although the Norman structure in turn is partly ruined, the massive Norman nave is still intact. It is topped by a Transitional triforium and, rising improbably above like the top-gallants of a full-rigged ship, by an Early English clerestory, the arcades in their entirety forming one of the finest examples of the conjunction of these architectural styles in Europe. In addition to the cathedral, Hugh Lupus built a stone castle on the site of an earlier motte. Then in 1090 the great Benedictine abbey was commenced. Since the Reformation it is this abbey which has become the cathedral of Chester, with much of its original monastic building still intact.

From the city walls of Chester one can look across Dee to the far hills and mountains of Wales, less than an hour's peaceful drive now, but an unconquered and threatening world apart then. Chester was the starting point for several military expeditions against the Welsh, notably the unsuccessful ones of King John in 1211 and Henry III in 1245. In 1277 Edward and a large army had clattered out of Chester's Northgate, crossed the Dee at Shotwick ford and, supported by a fleet, began the slow methodical campaign, emulating what Agricola had done twelve centuries previously, that eventually was to end in the amalgamation of Wales and England. For decades Chester remained Edward's secure supply base, channeling men and materials for his armies and for the building of the chain of the greatest medieval castles in Europe around the Welsh coast that acted as an effective stranglehold on the proud Welsh.

And there is much more to tell of Chester.

Of the Chester mystery plays, the earliest extant plays known in the English language, portraying the life and passion of Christ, first performed by the monks of the Abbey, then by the various guilds, banned in 1575 on account of their association with Roman Catholicism, but revived in recent years.

Of a grateful Edward's gift in 1300 of a Charter to his loyal city virtually establishing Chester as a city state, a fait accompli that was further recognised by Henry VII's "Great Charter" to the city in 1506. In 1301, Edward had decreed that his son, Edward of Caernarfon, should be known as Prince of Wales and Earl of Chester and for nearly seven centuries both titles have traditionally been held by a male heir to the throne.

Of a city loyal to her Stuart King Charles I, who watched from the north-east tower of Chester's walls the remnants of his army straggling back from defeat at the battle of nearby Rowton Moor in 1645. He then fled over Dee Bridge to Wales leaving Chester to suffer siege, battery, starvation, plague, and eventually conquest by the armies of Cromwell.

Of the last hurried refortification of the city in 1745 when the army of the Stuart Pretender Bonnie Prince Charlie invaded as far south as Derby, passing through nearby Manchester, before retreating to Scotland and bloody defeat at Culloden.

Of a city that has been the home of Dean Swift, Dr. Samuel Johnson, Handel, Henry James, and a favourite of many others, notably King William of Orange. James Boswell, friend and biographer of Dr. Johnson, mentioned in a letter of 1790: "Chester pleases my fancy more than any town I ever saw." Henry James's pen was more inspired: "Chester is still an antique town, and medieval England sits bravely under her gables. Every third house is a 'specimen' – gabled and latticed, timbered and carved, and wearing its years more or less lightly."

These and a great many other impressions of the gamut of British history formed and grew quickly and coalesced in my mind after my return to Britain and eventually became overpowering as I travelled around.

But, as I have mentioned, I often returned to Chester, a city herself now so old and burdened with history that perhaps she no longer cares, but is content merely to observe the range of human folly, and to speak softly to those who would listen to her. And maybe, when she speaks, she remembers the proud times long ago when she housed Rome's greatest Legion and, nearly a millennium later, the great sword, and was the conscience of our country.

It was here that disturbing outlines of our uncertain future, of which more anon, began to take shape in my mind as I sat quietly above the river in the gardens surrounding the ruins of the old cathedral and mused near the walls of the City of the Legions.

* * * * * * *

Know thyself

It was also during this period that, following the advice of the Delphic oracle, and having plenty of time to spare, I began to ask myself the question: Who was I? For many years of my life I had clearly danced, or wanted to dance, to a different tune from that heard by many of my colleagues. Some of them thought I was weird. For my part, I came to think that they were immature and inhibited, incomplete people in fact.

> The chief taboo of our industrial culture has been the fundamental exploration of questions of human progress, meaning and identity, and, indeed, of our own finiteness and death.
>
> Hazel Henderson

My life seemed to have comprised long periods without apparent purpose, be they conventional work or vagabonding, alternating with defining moments and the sudden lifting of veils and the pursuit of new paradigms.

It now at last finally dawned on me that I was born to worship Mother Earth. In doing this I was merely following in the footsteps of many before me.

In Mayan beliefs, for example, that persist to the present day, Earth is sacred, and the very reason for man's creation was that he might be a conscious bearer of respect for the Divinity of Earth.

And in the immortal words of Chief Seattle:

> This we know,
> The Earth does not belong to man,
> Man belongs to the Earth.
> This we know,
> All things are connected like the blood
> Which unites one family.
> All things are connected,
> And whatever befalls the Earth
> Befalls the sons of Earth.
> Man does not weave the web of life,
> He is merely a strand in it,

And whatever he does to the web,
He does to himself.

All this then was perhaps the reason that I had chosen to become a geologist (along with the irksome need to earn a living!) and that was why I had wandered over so much of Earth.

To Gaia, mother of all of life and oldest of gods, I sing,
You who make and feed and guide all creatures of the earth,
From you come our harvests, our children, our night and day,
Yours the power to give us life, yours to take away.
To you, who contain everything,
To Gaia, mother of all, I sing.

Homeric Hymn to Earth

The fact is, of course, that for more than 99% of the time that *Homo sapiens* has walked this planet, he and she have been hunter-gatherers in intimate contact with Nature of which they have regarded themselves as part. "Civilisation" and the twisted values involved in town-dwelling money societies have contributed to a fundamental dissociation of us from our psyches. It is an interesting question whether we might ever evolve into a psychically different species. I am sure that time is very much against us in this, even if it were possible, or even desirable. So would it not be far preferable therefore for us "civilised" folk to endeavour to come to some deep understanding and productive compromise with our psyches?

It seems to me now that, putting the matter in its lowest and most practical terms, we are going to have to learn how to unite in love for Earth in order for us to survive on Earth.

Touch the earth, love the earth, honour the earth, her plains, her valleys, her hills, and her seas; rest your spirit in her solitary places.

Henry Beston

This earth, this world . . . this lovely being, which is alive to its last recesses and understands my every feeling, soothed me, it cured me of my pains, and finally when I had fully understood my love for it, it taught me freedom.

Carlos Casteneda, *Tales of Power*

I have discovered the secret of your dream in the prairies, your serenity in the valleys, your will in the rocks, and your profound and mysterious silences in the caves . . . You are the tongue of eternity and the lips, You are the strings of the lute of centuries and the fingers, You are the idea of life and the symbol.

Khalil Gibran, *Hymn to the Land*

Clearly I am not alone. Others have travelled a similar path, some of them even more obsessively than myself and also capable of expressing themselves far more fluently than myself. A great many others must hear a similar call, at least at times. So, perhaps it is all a matter of degree. It may well just have been that accidents of predisposition, upbringing, spare time, travel, and opportunity permitted me the privilege, at last, to heed a call that is potentially within each of us.

To know oneself, therefore, is to come to terms with one's psyche. But people's psyches have much in common. So, to know oneself is to know humankind. Regrettably, it would seem that many of us today are too "busy" to discover the obvious. Even more regrettably, many are far too preoccupied with mere survival to be able to care.

But before we die, might we just ask the question which Cervantes's condemned fellow prisoners asked – not why they were to die, but why they had lived – and each had a story to tell.

* * * * * * *

A personal note

As regards accidents of predisposition and upbringing mentioned above, I must first acknowledge the prime influence of my parents.

My father was lame from birth. Tragically, I believe his lameness could have been corrected surgically while he was still very young, but his family were poor and the opportunity was lost. Although wiry and fit, he was not considered strong enough to farm. He was the one who went through school, where many years he won medals for 100% attendance. He left the Welsh Border and came to Liverpool and found a living as a cornmerchant's bookkeeper. He was highly regarded for his ability and honesty. These were not enough to save him from long unemployment when his firm went bust in the Great Depression (a business failure due in part to the dishonesty of directors, including a well-known titled figure). Eventually, he came back but never achieved the status and pay that he merited. I remember walking with him over the Wirral sand dunes one Sunday afternoon and coming upon a skylark's nest with four eggs in it. We carefully withdrew and waited for the skylark to return. I wish that his life could have been as carefree as that of a bird. But it wasn't. He used to bring me back cigarette cards from the office. Once he brought me a complete set of 50 birds, which he must have somehow obtained specially for me. I only saw my father really come to life when we went on the train to the farms in the Welsh Border for our holidays. That is where his spirit remained. He died on my twenty-first birthday. I was his only child. I remember him every day of my life. He taught me, among many other things, that honesty is unqualified.

> Do not go gentle into that good night.
> Rage, rage against the dying of the light.
>
> Dylan Thomas

My mother was a very capable and intelligent woman who, given different circumstances, might have enjoyed a very different life. But at the age of thirteen she had to carry her shoes to work in her first job in a milliner's with pay of one shilling a week. It was her taking over a small draper's shop near the Wallasey docks and starting a knitwear business there that kept food on our table in the 1930s. She remained very busy with this then and for many years afterwards. I believe she respected my father more than she loved him. Poor woman, she wanted me to be "successful" in life. Alas, I was often to prove a disappointment to her, but I had to go my own way. Her Irish mother and both brothers had all emigrated to the States and she was lonely. After she died at an advanced age, I found in her purse an old crumpled formal business card of mine with all the letters after my name – a silent record of a persona far removed from my true psyche. She was seventy years old before she told me of her illegitimacy. She found it difficult to understand that I only respected her the more for the cross she felt she had had to bear and conceal. She clung to convention and to secrecy about her parentage. Only rarely was I to enjoy any deep conversation with her, and that was when she was very old and her guard was relaxed.

For different but compelling reasons, therefore, both of my parent's spirits were shackled. Their spirits found their release, I believe, in me and, among many other things, spoke to me particularly of Wales and Ireland.

As for my upbringing, like many of my generation I experienced "culture shocks" at an early age. They were to break up and influence the pattern of my life considerably. At first, however, my school life was relaxed and fairly uneventful. I had been sent to the local convent school for my early education and quickly realised that, as a non-Catholic, I was different from most of the others. The Sisters were wonderful teachers and I owe a lot to them. One kind Sister told us that our pets could come to Heaven with us, but Head Sister Seraphine, made of sterner stuff, said that this was not true. I didn't know whom to believe; I knew whom I wanted to believe. This trivial incident had a great effect on me out of all proportion to its content. It made me question the wisdom and correctness of authority

(I have been told that I never lost this facility!). One Sister gave me a little brown geography book with a picture on its cover that I can visualise to this day of a city on a river near the sea, with the mountains behind in the hinterland. It made me want to enlarge my horizons and maybe one day climb those mountains and voyage that sea.

Then things got rough during the war. Children dropped out of school without notice. Sometimes it was due to a hurried evacuation. Once two of us walked to the home of two absent twins to see where they were, but when we got there we could see that their whole row of terraced houses had been obliterated by a landmine. We turned round and returned without speaking of the matter and never mentioned it afterwards. Later, close to Christmas, there was something rather final about having one's own home blasted, the tiny shop smashed in with its goods all over the street, the nearness of sudden death, the slow journey across the docks past burning warehouses, the walk along the bombed railway track, and the contrasting utter quiet and peace of the haven of Ty Newydd reached that same night.

There was something rather marvellous about not going to school and enjoying a hard winter snowed up on a Welsh hill farm without such luxuries as electricity and inside toilets. There were no books except a Bible. The only other reading matter was the *Farmer's Weekly* which was bought on Wednesday when the horse and cart went into town. On Sunday evenings it was dismembered for spills to light lamps and candles and for other purposes outside. The shiny pages were no good. The square glass accumulator for the wireless also went in to town every Wednesday to be recharged. It only had enough juice for us to be able to listen to the news and weather forecast once a day. Winter was followed by the miracle of Spring when the whole Welsh border is like a garden in paradise. When I left, my aunt gave me a book about Arthur, once king and king to be, which became one of my most prized possessions.

Afterwards came the remaining years of the war spent with a distant uncle who was a colliery secretary near Wigan. My schoolmates were rough, but I liked them. One friend came with a birthday present for me. It was a jigsaw of the *Wizard of Oz* and had cost sixpence at a time when pocket money was likely to be two or three pence a week at most. My aunt would not let him through the door because he was a miner's son. I think I became a socialist from that day forth. The process was consolidated by Jem, an ex-miner, broken in health in his forties, who was of all things our Sunday School teacher. Sunday afternoons were spent in listening to his tales of life in the pit and the iniquities of mine-owners. Many years later, as a college student, I thought I might return to work in the coalfield as a geologist, but wider horizons were to beckon.

Wigan holds many other memories for me. I remember often walking what seemed a long way to Pemberton Carnegie Library, past the pit and the mill and ruinous back-to-back terraced houses with their broken windows partially stuffed with paper and their half-naked urchins playing in the gutters. Carnegie provided another world. My reading was voracious. Biggles and William books were followed by Henty and Ballantyne, then Romany books, *Tarka the Otter*, and my first novel *How Green Was My Valley* and then Cronin's novels, Somerset Maugham's stories, Longfellow's poetry, etc., etc.

Some Saturdays a friend and myself used to cycle to Wigan Pier, chum up with some friendly bargee and his family and travel along the Leeds to Liverpool canal, riding on the narrow boat or cycling on ahead to help with the lock gates and sluices if they were set against us. We would often be given a mug of tea and once were given a groat to share.

Once, standing in a bus queue with my parents in the centre of Wigan, I remember a driver of the Royal Scot showing us his pay packet – under four pounds for a week's work. Another time I remember a Merchant Navy seaman who, against all odds, had survived several days adrift after being torpedoed in the North Atlantic in winter, telling us how his pay was stopped by the shipping company the day his ship had gone down [this, I have learnt later, was standard practice].

I remember a big lad in our class, a rival for the teacher's penny for best arithmetic of the week, who came to school in a threadbare sweater and holed shorts and pumps even in winter, sharing an orange with me in the depths of the war years. He died of TB. Years later, I remember meeting a lad I had once sat next to at Wigan Grammar School. He had been physically stronger than me then, but had been so weakened by years living in the grime of Makerfield that he appeared puny when I met him again in Oxford, whereas I had enjoyed the clean sea breezes of the Wirral coast only twenty-five miles away.

Towards the end of the war, I had returned to take my place as a scholarship boy at a Wirral grammar school that liked to boast of its direct-grant status (comparable to some of the present generation of "opted-out" schools). Many of the boys, whom some masters favoured even to the extent of dishonestly inflating their projected School Certificate marks, had got entry into the school not necessarily on the basis of merit but by their parents having paid for them for two prep years. It turned out also that the council had even fiddled the results of the 11-plus examination to allow boys from the "right" end of town to have unearned places in this grammar school. Although some boys were OK, by and large they were middle-class twits, fit only for eventual jobs in banking, insurance, and suchlike. The headmaster and I had an uneasy relationship over truancy and other acts of rebellion, a relationship which only softened when the school realised that I might be Oxbridge scholarship material, and thus could bolster their academic results. I never returned to school except once to thank two or three decent masters.

Among my neighbourhood friends at this time was the only son of a Norwegian widow whose husband had been lost at sea in the war. Nevertheless, the son went to sea as cabin-boy at the age of fourteen. He returned from his first voyage eight months later brown as a berry, wearing a matelot's hat, and with tales of boilers bursting in the China Sea and manning the rails with muskets to fight off pirates. Was I jealous!

Later, I was to find Oxford congenial, though I like to imagine that I never had the "character" and "breeding" of a typical Oxford student:

> The traditional upper class has maintained its power, wealth, and status by means of the "Oxbridge" system. Oxbridge – Oxford and Cambridge universities – is a social filter which weeds out lower-class undesirables and manufactures upper-class young men with good "character". At Oxbridge, an unwritten system of patronage and contacts recruits men for the most important posts in government, business, law, and the military . . . Easily identified from other Britons by their speech, dress, and manners, Oxbridge graduates acquire positions and advancement by reason of their wealth, social status, connections, and "breeding".
>
> Rodger J. Fadness in *The People's Almanac*

Unlike many people who are fortunate enough to retain lifelong links with childhood and school friends, my early life had thus been unusually segmented and disrupted. I was cut off from some conventional roots, perhaps one could say lonely, but I was free, free to live, and independent. Looking back, I think I value most those factors in my upbringing which encouraged me to be independent.

I used to day-dream obsessively in my late adolescence of finding a woman partner who would travel with me to the ends of the Earth and share in the discovery of Her secret places, but I never found her until much later. So I had to travel alone for much of my life. But, as I have said, my memories, now, are not of loneliness, but rather of the privilege of worshipping Earth.

* * * * * * *

Holy Places

So, having at last come to terms with myself, I had no qualms about surrendering myself to a continuing quest for Earth's holy places. Many of these have become so because of their associations with the spirits of previous seekers, but there are many which can be one's own personal holy places. And, of course, many holy places are Nature's alone.

The clean places

You must seek them alone, my son,
Among the spirits of forgotten men.
Where white-foamed seas arise to spindrift and a wheeling petrel,
Where sculptured rocks pierce pink snowfields and turquoise ice,
Where improbable oases moisten the spectral sand.
And the birds will have no fear of you,
Because you are not their equal there.
Should you return,
Friends may note the far look in your eyes,
And briefly wonder.

Significant above all for me seemed to be the mountains:

Mountains and memories, mandala and mantra

I will lift mine eyes
From Moelydd beyond silver Vyrnwy waters to Berwyn,
Just as I did as a child,
And find eternity alone.

I will lift mine eyes
Beyond the blue smoke from the turved house to Slieve Donard,
And find eternity alone.

I will lift mine eyes
Beyond the Isles of the Sea to Askival on the lonely isle,
And find eternity alone.

I will lift mine eyes
Beyond the cove of bluebells to Baccalieu,
And find eternity alone.

I will lift mine old eyes
Across sandy silvery Dee to the well-remembered Carneddau,
And find eternity alone.

And I will drift my thoughts
Beyond sight to my mind's eye,
To find eternity alone.

Eventually, I had little desire to extend travels, as more and more I came to realise that, for me at any rate, it was the Celtic fringe of Europe, and adjacent places that had come under its spell, that had most to offer me during my finite remaining time on Earth. Was it some kind of lingering race memory of the "Age of Saints", of whom I was to write a little book? My last travels before journey's end were thus a homecoming to Galicia, Brittany, Cornwall, Man, Galloway, the Hebrides, and particularly to Wales and Ireland.

> The Celtic parts of Britain are by far the poorer but they are also the most beautiful, and their poverty has enabled them to retain wider vision, the timeless sense of romance and the spiritual outlook denied to the busier and more prosperous communities.
>
> Nora Chadwick

All these places with their heady mixture of flowers, birds, megaliths, old saint's sites, a unique blend of history, spirituality, and nature, are lovely beyond compare for me, particularly in May and June time. I returned often to favourite walks in lonely coastal areas, or on lonely moorland tracks, or in ancient woodlands.

Above all, I was FREE !! Free to roam, free to dream. What a privilege! Sometimes I found myself imagining what my feelings would have been as a drover, or as a wandering Celtic monk, or as a Bronze Age trader.

> . . . our traveller steered his way along plateau and spur, past barrow and cairn and stone circle, by the sight of successive mountain tops. So guided, he reached his goal, the shore of a forgotten harbour, and saw against the sunset the black ships of the Irish.
>
> Cyril Fox

Within one busy period of twelve months I visited Skellig Michael, surely the most awesome physical setting in all Christendom, and many other ancient Celtic sites in western Ireland, and I lived on each of the three Holy Isles of Bardsey, Iona, and Lindisfarne for at least a week on each.

The week on Bardsey was perhaps the most significant. I was with a group who had gone there on retreat to meditate. They didn't mind at all if I went off by myself on some occasions. On one of these I fell asleep on the north shoulder of the hill, just where the Lleyn Peninsula comes into view, with its distinctive mountains marking the ancient route of pilgrims to Aberdaron whence they took ship for Bardsey. When I woke up, it was as if I was still dreaming. The only reality was the turf beneath my body, and the island below me with its nesting oystercatchers, lapwings, linnets, meadow pipits, gulls, choughs, and peregrine. The rest of the world was condensed to no more than the Lleyn Peninsula, itself floating suspended in a mist above the sea. There was nothing else in the world. I felt quite dizzy and lay in a dreamlike state for an unknown period of time.

On my last evening on Bardsey I joined the others in a vigil with chanting in the ruins of the ancient abbey. Then we were invited in turn to lay a small stone on the site of the old altar while each making a silent personal vow if we wished. Afterwards we pocketed our stones and all walked together in silence right round the island. When we had completed this, it was nightfall and a full moon was just rising. Later on that night, when the shearwaters had already begun to fly in with their weird cries, by the helpful light of the moon I stumbled up the hillside carrying my stone and laid it on the spot where I had experienced my vision.

My vow was to work for the remainder of my days so as to make a humble contribution to an ideal – that the love of Gaia might inspire the coming dark age just as the love of Christ had so unforgettably inspired the last one in this very same place.

PART IV FUTURE IMPERFECT

> There is a question in the air, more sensed than seen, like the invisible approach of a distant storm, a question that I would hesitate to ask aloud did I not believe it existed unvoiced in the minds of many: Is there hope for man?
>
> Robert Heilbroner, *An Inquiry into the Human Prospect*

Insights from geology

Casting now a wary eye to our future, I realise that the broad experience of geology has usefully taught me an enormous amount in this respect.

On a personal level, as a geologist I enjoyed living in many countries, not as a tourist but in a much more intimate manner. On rainy off-days in the bush I also enjoyed the luxury of peace and quiet to read and meditate. Sadly I also witnessed, first-hand, numerous instances of man's onslaught on Earth's natural resources. Indeed, I had been a participant.

> The conquest of the earth, which mostly means the taking it away from those who have a different complexion or slightly flatter noses than ourselves, is not a pretty thing when you think about it too much.
>
> Spoken by Marlow in *Heart of Darkness*, Joseph Conrad

> The history of mankind's development is a history of a consumer attitude toward nature.
>
> L. A. Piruzyon

On a professional level, geologists are obviously in a position to document the ongoing depletion of our natural resources on planet Earth.

But there are more subtle aspects of geology – a subject which some might superficially regard as "unscientific", because we do not experiment (Nature performed our experiments for us). Precisely because of this lack of direct experimentation, geologists have had to learn to observe, to theorise, and often to theorise afresh, keeping an open mind on various possibilities – scientific method personified! Geologists instinctively look to discern processes where others may just accept states.

I have already mentioned the very salutary experience of living through geology's great scientific revolution of the late 1960s. Now it matters relatively little when a new scientific theory is formulated and becomes accepted. But it matters a lot when irreversible and destructive processes are taking place on spaceship Earth, and we do little or nothing about our attitude towards them. What a wretchedly complacent creature is man.

Most importantly, it was geology that added the dimension of time to natural science. Decisively. Geology provided the detailed evidence of evolution, which is an established historical fact (although, granted, we may argue about the "how", and certainly cannot comprehend the "why" – if there is one). All this proved to be extremely controversial. Geologists perforce have had to learn to defend (still!) their honest and hard-won conclusions against ignorance, dogma, and superstition.

The fact is that we, that is to say members of the animal species *Homo sapiens*, happen to be but one of the four species of great apes on this planet. We are actually closely akin to chimpanzees in our DNA make-up. We are distinctive among the animal kingdom, however, in having evolved a large brain in proportion to our size. Our brain, furthermore, is unique in the pronounced development of the neocortex, the outer part of the brain that controls abstract functions such as thought. *Homo sapiens* has put a lot of its evolutionary eggs into this one basket of neocortex capacity.

This could prove to be a bizarre overspecialisation, a Faustian bargain in fact. It could quite likely result in the accelerated demise of our present civilisation, if not the extinction of our species (and Earth has already witnessed far more extinct species than those living today). Simply put, man may be too smart for his own good.

Two great scientific revolutions that will for ever be associated with the names of Copernicus and Darwin, when coupled with an appreciation of Gaia, should lead us away from a self-centred anthropocentric view to one of rational enquiry and humbleness in the face of Nature's handiwork.

We do *not* live on a flat Earth at the centre of the Universe! Man is *not* a unique creation of God, enjoying an implicit God-given mandate to exploit Gaia for his own purposes! There is *no* special providence that looks over our one miserable species! As Pliny the Elder put it:

> Now, That the soveraigne power and deity, whatsoever it is, should have regard of mankind is a toy and vanity, worthy to be laughed at. For can we choose to believe, can we make any doubt, but needs that Divinity and Godhead be polluted with so base and manifold a ministery?
>
> (from Philemon Holland's splendid translation, 1601)

If we have brains – and we do – then surely it should behove us to plan for a viable future, and show that there *is* intelligent life on Earth!

* * * * * * *

God, Gaia, time, and man

Let us then, with the help of a geologist's overview, add the dimension of time to Pliny's pithy comments on the relationship of man and the Deity. Imagine God keeping a diary about our one small planet. He (or She?) is interested in a great many others as well, so (let us say) He can only afford time to record the main events He sees on Earth. Let us suppose that the diary is in the form of a calendar of a year's duration and that it records events from Earth's origins up to, let us say, the year A.D.2000. Such a diary would read something like this.

In the first minute of January 1st there was a thermonuclear event, one of countless such in the Universe, which produced a central fireball surrounded by clouds of swirling outer debris. By mid January, Earth and the other planets had formed as recognisable nuclei among this debris. Until about mid March the surface of Earth was continually being bombarded by pieces of this debris producing flashes of light and giant craters. The bombardment gradually lessened and Earth's surface could be seen continually being broken up and affected in many places by volcanoes. By mid May Earth had a relatively stable crust.

By the end of July, those areas of Earth's surface above sea level began to assume a reddish tinge because the life processes of tiny marine algae had slowly produced an atmosphere containing oxygen which oxidised the surface rocks to a red colour. And God knew that planet Earth had become alive.

Things remained very much the same for a long time, except that the pattern of oceans and continents slowly changed as segments of the Earth's crust idly drifted around like pieces of scum on a viscously molten interior. Then, early in December, some areas of land near the coasts suddenly appeared green and by December 8th much of Earth's land surface was green. Soon, movement of animals, some of them very large, could be discerned among the green plant growth. Bombardment by debris had become increasingly rare but on the afternoon of 25th December there was a flash of light and Earth momentarily lost her greenness, only to recover it a split second later, when it could be seen that all the large animals had vanished. Miraculously, during the next few days, their place came to be taken by another conspicuous group of animals.

Beginning around 7 p.m. on the 31st December, Earth developed mantles of white at its two poles, and these mantles waxed and waned quickly along with changes in the relative extents of deserts (phenomena which had been observed before, on November 22nd and December 9th).

From 11 p.m. onwards on 31st December, small fires were observed to become much more numerous over much of Earth's surface, so much so that God suspected them somehow to be the work of one of the animals. At 3 minutes to midnight, tiny dark areas were observable near some big rivers on Earth. Close examination showed these areas to be swarming with a small animal. At 5 seconds to midnight, Earth's atmosphere, which had always clearly revealed a view of the lovely blue planet, became hazy. At 2 seconds to midnight three bright flashes were observed followed by several score others within the next second. At one second to midnight some kind of crisis was observable. Earth's green mantle was disappearing in many areas, large animals were noticeably fewer, deserts were increasing in many places and dark areas, curiously light by night, were observed to be increasing rapidly and swarming with the same verminous animal.

On closer investigation, God found out that many of the vermin had had the blasphemous impudence to represent Him in their own likeness, and to consider themselves favoured by Him over all the millions of His other animal species on Earth, even considering themselves to have recently been specially created by Him.

At this point, God's normally wry smile gave way to a frown. He was disturbed that this one verminous creature could apparently be so unappreciative of His overall creation, Gaia, and He thus became greatly concerned for the overall welfare of Gaia on Earth. He also ran out of space on the diary's last page, which is thus incomplete, and does not yet record the end of this true story of God, Gaia, time, and man.

* * * * * * *

Energy: the key to understanding

Energy is essential to all life. The story of the animal species *Homo sapiens* is how it has enormously increased its own numbers and raised its material living standards by ingeniously learning to harness various energy sources for its own use. Let us look at these in some detail.

The energy available to us on Earth derives ultimately from two leftovers of the thermonuclear event that gave birth to our solar system nearly five billion years ago. Of overwhelming importance, the first and very obvious "leftover" is our sun. Gaia depends on the sun. Plants, both land and marine, tap the sun's radiant energy (produced by ongoing nuclear fusion processes within the sun that will go on for another four billion years) by the process of photosynthesis. A simple chemical equation describes this:

Energy + water + carbon dioxide = plant + oxygen

Plant in this equation refers to the carbohydrate of plant tissue. The energy comes from sunlight. Water (plus some other minor but important nutrients) is obtained via a land-plant's root system. Carbon dioxide, a vital ingredient, is a gas present in tiny amounts in the atmosphere or dissolved in sea water. Oxygen, of course, is an abundant gas in the atmosphere. The animal kingdom eats plants, and some eat other animals, thus forming Gaia's food-chains in the sea and on land.

The above equation is reversible – that is to say, it works in the other direction as well. When it does so, it is called burning or oxidation or animal metabolism, according to the circumstances. Energy is then released, mainly in the form of heat. Forest fires are hot. So too, to a lesser degree, is a compost heap. We keep nicely warm and are able to exercise our bodies by digesting and metabolising food.

Our own personal energy needs can be readily quantified. We need roughly 1500 kilocalories of energy per day in the form of food intake solely to maintain bodily functions including breathing, circulation, and keeping warm. A fit person can regularly metabolise a variable amount up to around a further 4500 kilocalories per day (some such as Tour de France cyclists even more) and use all this for physical work. Few of us are as energetic as this, and some of us become obese by eating more than we need for the sparse exercise that we perform.

Man is unique among the animal kingdom in harnessing energy over and above what his own body can thus provide by food intake and metabolism. Fire was first utilised about 500,000 years ago for warmth and cooking. Much more recently, man has harnessed beasts (and slaves), wind power, and water power. Wind power was used mainly for the energy-intensive task of milling grain and also for pumping water, and was of course harnessed by sailing ships of a fascinating variety of design. Water power, as well as being used for milling, came to be ingeniously adapted for sawing, hammer mills, grinding, and so on. Charcoal was used to smelt metals from their ores, thus inaugurating the Bronze and Iron Ages.

The above are all "renewable" sources of energy. We will always have them. To them can be added the useful refinement of using water power to generate hydro-electricity, which is thus another renewable resource.

The industrial revolution was founded on coal-fired steam engines (and also, incidentally, on the wealth generated from slavery – economists once maintained that slavery was indispensable for economic health). Shed a tear for the passing of sail and another for the passing of steam. Both bred men. Since their time, we have developed internal combustion engines using oil fuels, and turbines now increasingly using natural gas.

Now coal, crude oil and natural gas (occurring with crude oil) are "non-renewable" resources of energy. Once burnt, they are gone. They represent, by long complex processes now understood by geologists, the fossilized remains of former plants and animals that have lived and died over a timespan of hundreds of millions of years – fossilized sun energy in effect. We are using up this limited and irreplaceable store of fossil fuel energy very, very quickly indeed.

It is salutary to pause and consider for a moment the consequences of the two great energy revolutions mankind has engineered on planet Earth.

The first, the agricultural revolution, harnessing *renewable* energy, resulted in a 100-fold increase in population (over that of preceding hunter-gatherer society). This was achieved gradually over about 8000 years and led to a population increase of half a billion humans.

The second, the industrial revolution, harnessing *non-renewable* energy, although "only" resulting in a 10-fold increase in population (over that of preceding agricultural society), has been achieved in less than 300 years. It has led to a staggering population increase of five and a half billion humans, with the prospect of more increase to come because of the present age structure of population in many countries.

Energy use is characteristic of, and indispensable to, our present industrial society. We are now "hooked" on energy and use it on a massive scale.

To illustrate this, consider first food, our most basic need. Hunter-gatherers, or peasants growing rice with the aid of buffalo in a rice paddy, and cooking on a wood fire, can achieve ratios of up to 20 to one. That is to say, they may obtain or produce 20 units of energy (in the form of food) for every unit of work energy they themselves expend, clearly a good bargain in terms of energy. In the USA, on the other hand, approximately 10 units of energy, mainly of the non-renewable kind, are expended for every unit of food energy that arrives on the table. In terms of energy expenditure, this is thus an up to 200 times worse scenario.

In addition to eating, we keep houses, shops, and business premises warm (or cool), we travel, we enjoy various appliances, and we drive vehicles that are energy-costly to manufacture and to run.

Furthermore, the industrial use of energy is prodigious. The mining and processing of metals accounts for nearly 20% of the total energy used by an advanced industrial society. A significant 14% of oil and gas production is now consumed in an incredibly diverse petrochemical industry including the manufacture of fertilizer, plastics, herbicides and pesticides. And so on. Much of what is profit for industry and trade derives ultimately from cheap fuel.

Very quickly therefore, we realise how utterly dependent our industrially developed societies have become on the massive use of non-renewable energy. The policy of industrialised countries has been to relentlessly exploit available energy resources, and indeed other natural resources, obtained from both within and without their own borders. One has to say that this has generally been done without thought for a sustainable future, only for profit, and has at times led to adventures in foreign policy.

As an illustration of the link between energy use and material wealth, the per capita use of energy in North America is twice that of Europe, twenty times that of India, and well over fifty times that of the poorer African countries. I am not an admirer of the gentleman responsible for the following quotation, but on this occasion he was telling the plain truth, albeit qualified by a wish (hinted threat?) at the end:

> There are only 6 percent of the people in the world living in the United States [actually, now more like 4%], and we use 30 percent of all the energy. That isn't bad; that is good. That means we are the richest, strongest people in the world, and that we have the highest standard of living in the world. That is why we need so much energy, and may it always be that way.
>
> Richard Nixon, November 1973

World-wide, we now use energy at a per capita rate over six times that of the year 1900. World population is increasing. It more than quadrupled in the 20th century. In the year 2000 we thus find ourselves using well over 25 times as much energy world-wide as in the beginning of the century in the year 1900.

Alarmingly, about 85% of the energy we now use is of the *non-renewable* kind. Even the rate of fuelwood use now is greater than that of *all* energy use in the year 1900! The present breakdown by major categories of energy use is approximately as follows:

Oil	33%
Gas	21%
Coal	26%
Hydro	6%

Nuclear	5%
Wood	5%
Miscellaneous	4%

It is worth mentioning that the contributions of hydro power and nuclear power have, following convention, each been inflated threefold in arriving at the percentages in the above list. The reason for doing this is for comparative purposes. Both nuclear and hydro power produce electricity and, due to the workings of the second law of thermodynamics, if electricity is produced from plants fired by oil, gas, or coal, only about one-third of the intrinsic heat energy of these fuels can be converted into electricity.

Miscellaneous sources of renewable energy, apart from wood and hydropower, comprise in decreasing order: animal power, manpower, crop residues, animal dung, geothermal, wind, energy crops, solar collectors, and tidal power.

Three major questions arise:

1. How long will our *non-renewable* energy resources last?
2. If necessary, could we eventually substitute wood, hydropower and other *renewable* energy resources for them?
3. Could nuclear power be the ultimate answer for our energy needs?

Answers are as follows:

1. Geologists are now able to estimate that, making informed estimates of the totals that we can ever expect to discover and extract in the future, at present rates of consumption conventional oil would last 120 years, gas a little longer, and coal perhaps for as much as 400 years. These, it should be emphasized, are best estimates for *totals* that might *ever* be extracted from all possible geological structures, including those yet to be discovered and proved. For example, we actually have only about 40 years supply of conventional oil in sight at present. The figure for oil could possibly be augmented by "non-conventional" oil. The latter refers to oil obtainable from tar sands and oil shales, albeit at considerable cost and unavoidable "energy-cannibalisation" involved in its extraction.

2. Wood, the indispensable energy resource for the domestic needs of about half of the world's people, is already being used at unsustainable rates. As we have noted, this is leading to catastrophe in the Gangetic catchment area and indeed in a great many other areas. Forests, as once perceptively remarked by Chateaubriand: "precede civilisation while deserts follow."

There is some potential for increased hydropower, albeit subject to the eventual silting up of many dams. With some very optimistic assumptions its contribution could perhaps be doubled.

There are severe practical limitations on other renewable sources of energy (appealing as the prospect of increased wind and tidal power, direct solar energy, etc., may be). At best, it would seem that they would scarcely be able to supply more than a few extra percent of industrial society's massive current energy usage.

3. Nuclear power (the most controversial) is dependent on Earth's one naturally occurring fissionable isotope, uranium 235. This is the second "left-over" from the thermonuclear event that gave us our solar system, and minuscule in proportion to the sun's energy. This unique isotope, technically both a mineral and a fuel, constitutes only seven-thousandths of natural uranium. Uranium itself is a very rare element, present in the Earth's crustal rocks to the extent of less than two parts per million. As well as the problem of finding suitable ore deposits of this rare material, and the costs (and cannibalistic energy expenditure!) of mining and processing the large volumes of rock necessary to obtain the uranium and concentrating the desired isotope, nuclear power suffers from several other inherent grave disadvantages.

Nuclear power stations are extremely costly to build and insure. In the USA it is now over twenty years since a new nuclear power plant was commissioned. Nuclear power will never be the energy saviour of Third-World countries on the grounds of expense alone.

More worryingly, nuclear power involves seemingly intractable problems of the ongoing safe disposal of radioactive waste and the eventual decommissioning of reactors. These problems have yet to be honestly faced. The potential for catastrophic accidents also cannot be ignored. Neither can the potential of nuclear power plants for fabricating atomic weapons and for terrorism.

Progress in the development of so-called "fast", alias "breeder", reactors (that involve the processing of spent uranium fuel to recover fissionable plutonium) has faltered on the grounds of even higher expense and of the severe technical problems of handling liquid sodium as the heat-exchange liquid. There is also the problem of unavoidable dangerous pollution associated with the complex "reprocessing" that is necessary to extract the plutonium from the spent uranium. The reprocessing plant at Sellafield, UK, for example *routinely* discharges more radioactive waste into the atmosphere and the sea than does the *whole* of the rest of the nuclear industry of Europe combined. This is apart from hushed-up accidental discharges.

Fusion, as opposed to fission, remains still a pie-in-the-sky dream.

My conclusion, after long study of a complicated problem, is that the nuclear industry (obscenely allied with the production of nuclear weapons) has lied through its teeth about pollution hazards and much else, and that it would have been better for mankind if uranium 235 had gone the way of many other radioactive isotopes and decayed away before Homo sapiens appeared on the scene! One more Three Mile Island or Chernobyl could prove to have a decisive effect on public opinion, especially if it should happen in densely populated Europe (which also has the world's densest concentration of nuclear power stations). Meanwhile, we can only wait and see.

Given these unresolved and disturbing answers to the three questions posed above, why is an energy crisis not apparent to everyone?

The answer lies in the fact that at the moment our production *capacity* for oil and natural gas (that together constitute easily our major energy source at present) is high. Prices in the last years of the 20th century have reflected this and have remained therefore very low.

This high production capacity arises because a large proportion of the world's oil and gas happens to occur in a relatively small number of huge fields that have been very easy to find and extremely cheap to exploit. As a working rule of thumb, oil fields on land (except the very largest) are exploited at a rate so as to yield half of their oil in 12 years. For offshore oil fields, where development costs are higher, the aim is for even more rapid exploitation, half in 7 years. Money talks. The enormous profitability of the world's mammoth oil industry has completely overshadowed legitimate concerns about its sustainability in the longer term.

The ensuing comfortable energy situation at present – humankind has never had such abundant and cheap energy as in the second half of the 20th century – is thus very much a fool's paradise. Long, long before 120 years are up (as mentioned above, the most optimistic life for our total supplies of conventional oil at current rates of consumption), a shortfall in oil supply will become apparent. Production will slowly but inexorably begin to falter below the level of current demand and prices will begin to rise sharply in response to this.

Historically, the price of crude oil has always been prone to severe price swings. This is because high exploration costs mean that producers of oil want to see some return on their investment and will sell oil at virtually any price to maintain some cashflow even at times when there may be an oversupply. Conversely, if oil is in short supply, even slightly, it is impossible for producers to suddenly increase production from the existing stock of oil wells. The position can of course be complicated by the action of swing producers such as OPEC (actually mainly Saudi Arabia).

One brave and fascinating analysis by a recently retired senior oil geologist, *The Coming Oil Crisis* by Colin J. Campbell, predicted in 1997 that the subtle but fundamental changeover from a scenario of comfortable oversupply of oil to one of continuing undersupply would likely occur early in the first decade of the present century.

The resulting effect of any significant increase in the price of crude oil would obviously be painful throughout the rich industrial world. In those many parts of the Third World where kerosene is the only feasible alternative to vanishing resources of wood for essential domestic needs, such an increase would be catastrophic. As I write in early 2001, Colin Campbell's prediction would appear to be only too prescient.

In trying to understand our oil economy, it is very instructive indeed to look at the well documented history of oil production in the USA. An early leader in the field of oil, the USA was producing 70% of the world's oil in 1925. This proportion had shrunk to a still considerable 50% in 1955. By this time, however, despite the application of increasingly sophisticated prospecting techniques, the rate of discovery of new oil reserves each year had decreased and had come to fall and remain below annual production levels. Clearly, this was and is an unsustainable situation. Nevertheless, already proved reserves at that time were very high, and oil continued to be pumped like there was no tomorrow, reaching a maximum production of 11.3 million barrels per day in 1970.

Since then, annual production from the lower 48 States has steadily and inexorably declined year on year to a level of 6.8 million barrels per day in 1999. This fall in production has occurred in spite of enormous inducements being offered to oil developers in the Reagan years, and the number of oil-producing wells having now risen to the prodigious figure of over 600,000. The lower 48 States of the USA thus resemble an extremely well-used (please excuse the pun) pin cushion, as far as drilling for oil is concerned. Consequently, the likelihood of any further substantial discoveries of oil there is remote. In fact, 53 of the 57 known giant oil fields there were discovered before the time of World War II.

Now there is the old saying "many a mickle makes a muckle", but the experience of the oil industry worldwide is that most of the world's recoverable oil *is* concentrated in a surprisingly small number of large "giant" fields (defined as having over 500 million barrels of oil each). The fact is, of course, that a wildcat exploration well on a small potentially oil-bearing structure costs just as much to drill as one exploring a larger structure with potentially greater rewards. Eventually, the game becomes not worth the candle. And the costs (including real energy costs) of frontier exploration can be high. As an illustration of this, the cost of just one (unsuccessful) wildcat well drilled by BP on a promising structure in the Arctic offshore of the Mackenzie delta was a staggering $130,000,000.

It is apparent therefore that we just cannot look to a tail of aggregate production from a large number of small fields to maintain production at high levels after the giant fields have been found and exploited. The experience of the USA, now explored for oil to a far greater extent than anywhere else in the world, demonstrates all this well, and would thus seem to provide a sober preview of things to come on a global scale.

Interestingly, the total current US production of about 8.0 million barrels per day (production from the 48 States now augmented by production from the relatively recently discovered supergiant Prudhoe field in Alaska) contrasts with current US consumption running at 18.5 million barrels per day. The importation of the shortfall of 10.5 million barrels a day at the current price of roughly $26 per barrel costs about $100 billion dollars per year. This is the biggest single item in a now chronic US trade deficit which is unsustainable and which is threatening to destabilise the world economy.

Clearly, our energy situation is likely to prove increasingly critical in the future. We have actually already passed the time of one high-water mark of our energy situation. Curiously, it has not attracted much comment. But on a worldwide per capita basis, energy consumption actually peaked in 1979 (data from British Petroleum's excellent annual *Statistical Review of World Energy* and from United Nations publications on world population).

Now I don't dispute – indeed, I would advocate – that we could still learn to enjoy decent and civilised lives while perforce all gradually using less energy. But the future is not likely to work like that. The reasons for this have a lot to do with increasing inequity in our unprecedented and very ugly worldwide "money" society, of which more anon.

Energy is a complex topic. I could explain a lot more. I did in my book that was never published. To some extent, a lay reader is going to have to accept my assertion on trust that our global industrial economy and the lifestyles we have predicated on it will falter because of a lack of abundant cheap energy. A few, a very few, geologists, some far more eminent than myself, have been attempting to draw attention to this for some time now – a great many more, alas, are muzzled by sundry pressures.

> As an event in geological history we may well ask which is the more remarkable phenomenon, for the earth to accumulate the stores of coal and oil during 600 million years, or for a single animal species to destroy them within a span of three centuries?
>
> M. King Hubbert

* * * * * * *

Evidence before our eyes

> Our terrestrial habitat . . . is pillaged and devastated by a poor majority that destroys its resources simply to live from day to day, and by a rich minority that insatiably consumes and wastes them. The one cannot think about tomorrow, the other simply does not care about it.
>
> Aurelio Peccei

A final energy crunch may not come quickly, but when it comes it will prove decisive. I shall be dead before it arrives, along with today's politicians. The probable time frame is such that it will very likely bother my children. My grandchildren, in their despair, will wonder why we refused to see it coming and had at least begun to take some sensible steps in preparation for it.

The scenario with minerals (which originally sparked my own concerns in natural-resource matters) is comparable to that of energy resources. An optimistic [sic] article some years ago reckoned that with luck in new discoveries, advances in refining and processing ores, development of alternatives for those metals in shortest supply, and *assuming adequate energy resources* [my italics], resources of ores of most essential metals might last until the end of this century. The fact is, of course, that much of the richest and most accessible mineral ore has already been mined out, often leaving behind an ugly hole in the ground and a local social problem. There is plenty of iron ore and aluminium ore but these are energy-intensive to smelt, aluminium ore particularly so. And there are many other metals which are essential to industry which will prove to be in short supply.

The foregoing has all had to do with our "non-renewable" resources. As I have mentioned, once used, they are gone for ever (apart from a limited degree of possible recycling of metals).

If anything, problems with our (technically) "renewable" resources are, paradoxically perhaps, even more pressing. I say *technically* renewable because in fact there are limits.

You can cut down trees faster than forest can regenerate. You can overfish. You can extract groundwater quicker than it can be replenished. You can put pressure on supplies of fresh water by the sheer amount of human waste and by pollution. You can plough marginal land and then suffer catastrophic dustbowls and loss of irreplaceable topsoil in the dry years which will surely come sooner or later. You can irrigate and eventually cause land to become unusable due to a rise in the water table and ensuing salinisation. You can continue to put more stock on common grazing land to the point where there is just not enough grass for them all, although it may obviously be to each herdsman's advantage to attempt to increase his own stock (Gilbert Harding's famous "Tragedy of the Commons" dilemma).

In an attempt to preserve God's good fresh air, you can build a tall chimney to disperse industrial waste from a local site, only for an aggregate of waste gases, smog and acid rain from similar waste to affect whole regions and our global weather. I think by now most people realise how prone to adverse change is our fragile atmosphere as a result of gross man-made pollution. The atmosphere is after all equivalent in mass to a layer of water around the surface of the earth a mere thirty feet thick.

Not only *can* these kinds of things happen, they *are* happening in our world of today. A particularly poignant example is that it makes "economic sense" to use the capital tied up in whaling fleets to hunt and kill many species of whales to virtual extinction for quick profits, say within the working life of the ships. The reason is that these quick profits can easily have a value greater than that of a more modest but sustainable annual catch, *even for ever*. A student of mine once documented this apparent paradox in detail, using the concept of "present value" familiar to economists, mortgagees, mining developers, and others dealing with money and profit. The rest of the class were first incredulous and then disgusted, but she was right. Basically, the apparent paradox arises from the fact that a whaler, after making a quick and profitable killing, could take his capital augmented by *quick* profits elsewhere to a different enterprise in order to earn more profits for him at, let us say at a rate of 10%, whereas rates of maturing and breeding of whale species may only be enough to support a sustainable annual cull of 3% or less of the whale population.

Although I have emphasized that our future is fundamentally and inextricably based on our use/abuse of natural resources, both renewable and non-renewable, there are other grounds for great concern. These have to do with the social conditions under which much of humankind now exists, and under which many more are coming to exist.

The first concern is the unprecedented level of human population and its continuing rise. One startling statistic is that every seven years we are currently adding (*excess* of births over deaths) another half billion humans, a number equivalent to Earth's entire human population around the year 1650. The next generation of mothers has already been born, and it is by far the largest that there has ever been (the so-called "pyramid effect").

That these large numbers are being fed at all is largely due to the success of the "Green Revolution". Largely unsung because of its mix of mainly unspectacular "soft" technologies, it has been overwhelmingly important. It has been based principally on the development of high-yielding hybrid grain seeds, grown ideally on irrigated land, nurtured by fertilizers and protected by pesticides. Not only are there inherent dangers and drawbacks in all this, stemming in large part from a lack of genetic diversity in the marketed seeds, but there *are* limits to production. Per capita grain production (a realistic measure of world food supply), after rising dramatically in the 1950s and 1960s, and then steadying over the subsequent two to three decades, is in fact now declining to below the 1970 level.

To illustrate how resource problems can be compounded by population changes, during the fifteen minutes or so that it may take you to read this section, the population of Pakistan will have increased by 60, and 3 acres of prime irrigated land of the vast Indus Valley plains will have gone out of production permanently, due to salinisation. And the scales will continue to swing this way every fifteen minutes, this day, this month, this year, and so on with no prospect of change for the better in sight.

Significantly, the Green Revolution has benefitted most those with capital, who can afford expensive hybrid seeds (many of which have to be purchased afresh each year), machinery, fertilizer, etc. Many people are surprised to learn that the world's largest seedsmen are now the multinational oil and chemical companies who, very conveniently, also manufacture and sell the (expensive) fertilizers and pesticides that are essential for the "miracle" seeds. They have contrived to up the price of seeds, too! – at rates considerably in excess of inflation. The controversial introduction of genetically modified seeds is a continuation of this same trend. The immense profitability and vested interests in all the above inhibit research in other areas that could be of benefit to mankind, for example the selective breeding of plant species which could produce consistently in the commoner, less ideal conditions than those demanded by the miracle hybrid seeds.

Now that agriculture has become "agribusiness" with much costly up-front expenditure, the ownership of good land tends to fall increasingly into the hands of the wealthy few with capital. Jobs on the land fall due to mechanization, and the numbers of landless increase. The continuing amazing emigration to urban conurbations is now not so much pulled by opportunities for work there but pushed by rural despair.

World-wide, urban population is increasing at an even greater rate than that of total population. It reached 50% of total world population in the year 2000, compared with around 15% in 1900 and 2% in 1800. So, as wryly noted by God in our earlier parable, man is fast becoming an urban animal.

The number of urban dwellers is increasing by over one million *every week*. Nearly all of this increase accrues to the cities and towns of Third World countries. Just reflect on the amount of *extra* houses, schools, hospitals, public transport, water supply, sewerage, and other services necessary to cope with this increase. The sad fact is that they don't cope. In many countries of the Third World the conditions of urban poverty have to be experienced to be believed. Unemployment, underemployment, exploitation, shanty towns, lack of sanitation, unsafe water, sickness, disease, absence or unaffordability of medical care, and crime are the common lot of many of their city inhabitants. For them, cities are now becoming Earth's disgusting and wasteful cancers in which life is a surrealist nightmare.

Already densely urbanised, albeit generally in relatively good conditions, the peoples of the rich world are now increasingly coming to experience malaise. In some countries, taxation from a dwindling industrial sector can no longer pay for acceptable levels of social services, decent education, and health care for all citizens. Precious capital tends to be exported in order to exploit cheaper labour and poorer environmental and safety controls in Third World countries. Ensuing trade deficits are in part made up by the export of hideous weapons of war (world "defence" expenditure currently totals over $800 billion per annum). Corruption thrives. People become apathetic, alienated, and cynical about defects in their society and their government's seeming inability to do anything about them. Mental disorders and deviant behaviour, akin to those observed in overcrowded rats, proliferate. Under these conditions the hopelessness of the poor affects the rich, both within and across state frontiers in such areas as "economic" migration, drug trafficking, infectious disease, poisoned food, vandalism, and crime. Quality of life may thus eventually come to be eroded for everyone, rich or poor. An increasingly motorised lifestyle in many of the developed countries will prove to be not sustainable, and we will tend to be left with a legacy of useless suburban sprawl.

What is even more worrying is that under urban conditions, ranging as they may between incredible extremes of poverty and affluence, humankind is becoming increasingly divorced not only from its psychic roots but also from any realistic first-hand appreciation of natural resources. Everything tends to become subordinated to the quest for money, and the real basis for constructive ideas for a viable future is being lost.

* * * * * * *

Money – the root of much evil

> Children, how hard is it for them that trust in riches to enter into the kingdom of God.
>
> Mark, 10:24

> Property is theft.
>
> Saint Basil

It was the prehistoric agricultural revolution that first led to surplus production and acquisition of possessions. To a large extent, these were unnecessary, indeed a nuisance, in preceding hunter-gatherer society – one only had to carry them about! The industrial revolution led in turn to capitalism and the possibility of undreamt of wealth, at least for a few. But in our world of today a very great many more have become utterly destitute. This gross inequity is attributable in large part to money and, it has to be said, to the capitalist system that so worships it.

Like many others I suppose I just lived with and accepted "money" and "price" and never thought about the subject. Now that I perceive the nature of money in our contemporary society and, even more importantly, the implications of the *fatal link* of money to land and Earth's other finite natural resources by the mechanism of price, I am concerned, even horrified.

When did money begin? It appears that the first coins were minted from electrum, an alloy of gold and silver in about 625 B.C. in the kingdom of Lydia, a civilised agricultural society situated in what is now western Turkey. The obvious use of this money was to supplement barter transactions and to facilitate trade. Coins could readily then be exchanged in the market place for food, baskets, beer, woven cloth, leather goods, domestic animals, implements, jewellery, etc. One can get a feel for this historic and legitimate use of money by experiencing a rural souk on a busy market day in a country such as Morocco, for example.

No currency in the world is now linked to something which is regarded of intrinsic value, such as one of the precious metals. Although linked by the mechanism of "price" in the marketplace to natural resources and goods derived therefrom, money is printed (on intrinsically valueless paper) and minted (now entirely in base metals) by governments at rates which bear no essential relation to the Earth's finite stock of natural resources. Naturally, people lose their faith in this money, prices rise, and we have inflation. For many years, the good and wise dons of Oxford had their salaries paid not at some nominal figure in money, but at a rate equivalent to the price each year of a designated number of bushels of wheat. At least, they would not starve in times of inflation! Most of us today have to depend on annual wage increases to keep abreast of inflation. Pious lip-service to the economic fiction (one of many) of "money supply" generally restrains inflation rates to the single figures we are now accustomed to living with. Sometimes, as for example with some exceptionally dishonest and/or financially strapped governments, inflation rates can become uncomfortably high.

Inflation, whether gradual or galloping, is the inevitable revenge of (finite) natural resources inflicted upon lenders of (dishonest) money printed by (unmentionable) governments.

Incidentally, for proof of the dishonesty of today's paper money, you have merely to reach into your pocket and pull out a banknote. On it, in small print, just to the left of the portrait of our gracious sovereign, you will see the following categorical statement: "I promise to pay the bearer on demand the sum of FIVE POUNDS" [or whatever denomination of note you may have chosen], personally signed below by the Chief Cashier on behalf of the Bank of England. Now I have never myself presented a banknote to the Bank of England and demanded my five pounds, for the good reason that I know very well that they could not in fact redeem my note, as they promise, for five pounds. The point is that they could have, once. In Victorian times, indeed up until 1914, one could have received a gold sovereign for a pound note. Even as recently as 1967, it was possible to take a dollar bill into any Canadian bank and demand and receive a silver dollar for it. The market value of those coins as bullion was then pretty close to a pound and a dollar respectively.

Money, interest, and profits come to be highly regarded by people who form the affluent and powerful upper classes in capitalist societies. Indeed, all this often forms the main focus of their existence. The very rich have so much money that they may be obliged to lend some of it to dishonest borrowers such as governments who have neither the intention nor the means of repaying it (except by borrowing more in order to do so!) *What all lenders should not forget is that money is ultimately useless unless it can be translated in a market place into tangible assets.* These in turn are derived from natural resources, and Earth's natural resources are finite. Nearly 100 billion Pounds changes hands on an average day in the London money market. How often, I wonder, does the question of natural resources enter the minds, even for a moment, of those who make their lucrative livings in this frenzied activity?

While natural resources, particularly energy resources, are abundant and cheap, business is profitable. Indeed, that is one of the reasons why our capitalistic societies have arisen and thrived. Extended periods of profitable business enterprise encourage people and businesses to borrow in order to pursue an economic growth that seems both desirable and inevitble. Yearly rises in Gross National Products are welcomed. Debt tends to increase, often at a faster rate than the increase of goods and services, and hence profits. More and more profits have to go towards servicing debt, which may come to approach, equal, or even exceed liquid assets in amount. In these circumstances, money becomes more expensive, that is to say interest rates rise, as euphoria eventually yields to nervousness in the minds of investors. Banks, however, continue to lend money because this is what they are used to doing, and paradoxically because further lending may be the only way for their outstanding loans to be serviced! The banks may even lend money to each other and then use this network of loans as collateral to bolster their paper assets, thus further endangering a collapse of the whole pack of cards.

Eventually, because of the inexorable cumulative effect of all this, catalysed as it is by greed, perhaps in the end triggered by sudden panic among investors, by war, or by scarcity and price rise of natural resources, much of the debt burden is wiped out by an interlinked series of business failures and defaults on loans.

The first large speculative boom tied to money trading was "Tulip Mania" that raged for four years in 17th century Holland. An engaging account of this is given by Dr.D.G.Hessayon in his *Armchair Book of the Garden*. Promissory notes to supply tulip bulbs (like our present-day "futures" markets) came to be actively traded in Bruges at the house of the van der Beurse family (hence the term "bourse"). Intense speculation pushed the price of such notes upwards, numerous people participated, and some became millionaires. Eventually, in April 1637 the Dutch government decreed that all notes had to be honoured and the promised bulbs supplied that season. Regrettably, it turned out that there were more promissory notes than bulbs and the market in notes collapsed. "Rich men became paupers overnight, and suicides were common." With the wisdom of hindsight, we see in this relatively uncomplicated example how a ludicrous divorce of paper wealth from natural resources led to an inevitable conclusion.

Similar cycles of over-optimistic speculation led to the well-known "South Sea Bubble" collapse of 1720, to the boom and bust railway era of early Victorian times and, very recently, to the collapse of share prices of stocks in information technology.

This kind of recurring catharsis, if sufficiently pronounced and widespread, is called a depression. Although a few financiers may jump into Wall Street without parachutes, guess who suffers most from depressions, which have proved to be characteristic features of a capitalistic money economy? Depressions may rob a few lenders of their money – they may rob very many workers of jobs and hope. This brings us, not before time, to a consideration of capitalism.

* * * * * * *

The nature of capitalism

> A fella in business got to lie and cheat but he calls it somepin else.
>
> John Steinbeck in *Grapes of Wrath*

Capitalism is the process of maximising monetary profits by whatever methods in the shortest possible term for those who already possess capital or have access to it.

To this end, a capitalist business enterprise, for example, aims to sell the cheapest, shoddiest product that it can get away with at the maximum price that it can extort, while paying as little wages as it can to labour, with little or no heed to the social injustice that it may create, or to the depletion of the natural resources that it may harness, or to the environmental damage that it may cause. An unflattering picture, perhaps exaggerated, but alas basically true in many respects.

Whatever may be the personal virtues of individuals living in a capitalist society, capitalism itself thus has no intrinsic moral virtue whatsoever as it is geared only to monetary profit. Any social virtue it might have retained, for example as a result of personal commitment between employer and employee in a small-scale business enterprise or between retailer or tradesman and customer, tends to disappear in today's world of big business, accountants and company lawyers, short-sighted and corrupt trade unions, takeover bids, share options and sleaze. Of course, governments may step in with such things as tax laws, monopoly commissions, trading standards, environmental controls, labour legislation and the like, but these usually prove to be only minor irritants to capitalism, and governments can be lobbied, threatened, or bought.

Some would doubtless be quick to point out that industrial capitalism has resulted in more affluence for more people than ever before, and previously undreamt of amenities for many, including education, leisure, travel, health facilities, freedom from infectious disease, etc. Also, many people, at least up until quite recently, have enjoyed steadily increasing personal affluence. All this is true. But, there are also more unemployed, destitute, starving, illiterate, and hopeless people in the world than ever before, many of them without access even to the natural resource of land, and their numbers are steadily increasing.

This pronounced *inequity* is indeed one of the distinctive features of a laissez-faire capitalistic society. It was for example, the gross contrast between the fortunate wealthy (many of them nouveaux-riches capitalists) and an incredibly exploited work-force of impoverished men, women, and children that led to the emergence of great humanitarian and social reform movements in 19th century Britain.

Why should there be this tendency towards gross inequity? The answer is that the prime aim of capitalism is to increase the capital of those already possessing it. To the extent of concentrations of capital in relatively few private hands, others must be relatively deprived. This is because we live in a world of ultimately finite natural resources (the basis of true "wealth"), no matter how beneficially and ingeniously we may attempt to exploit them. Indeed, the word private comes from the Latin *privare*, which means to deprive. The trouble with capitalism is not that it doesn't work, as some socialists were fond of declaiming, but, given its selfish and short-sighted aims, that it works too well!

So the question really becomes: How does capitalism work so well – for the fortunate possessors of capital, at least?

The reason is quite simply that the power structures in capitalist societies work so as to provide or allow conditions favourable for making money profits. As a capitalist in a capitalist society therefore, once you have enough capital-generated income to supply your personal needs, you cannot help but get richer, unless you should waste your capital by extravagance, or should be very imprudent with investments. Indeed, once very rich, it is virtually impossible to avoid getting even richer, even if one is an ignorant wastrel and spendthrift.

> The legal and administrative system of the late empire favoured economic tyranny. It was in the power of a rich man to deprive a poor man of all he possessed.
>
> from *Roman Britain and the English Settlements*
> by R.G.Collinwood & J.N.L.Myers

So pronounced is this tendency to inequity in a capitalist society, once it is entrenched it is impossible to eradicate it by constitutional means. Even enlightened measures such as progressive taxation and the attempted provision of social services for all in our contemporary "mixed" economies do not fundamentally change things in this respect. Those with most capital will inevitably get richer quicker and thus maintain and increase the differential in wealth between themselves and those with little or no capital. Of course, while cheap natural resources remain available and overall affluence increases as a result of their exploitation, even many of the relatively underprivileged wage-earners in a capitalist society may come to find themselves materially better off – for a while.

It is instructive in this respect to consider the example of the USA, which is not only the largest and richest single economic power in the world, but also exhibits a mature capitalist industrial society. Some would maintain that the one follows logically from the other. And it is indisputable that in the USA a great many decent people live comfortable lives.

Nevertheless, capitalism has led, predictably, to enormous inequity in American society. As an illustration of this, 80% of all common stock is owned by under 1% of the population, while somewhere between 15% and 20% of the population exist below various recognised poverty levels. The proportion of children recognised to be living in poverty is higher – a full 20%.

Other tangible reflections of inequity are widespread. A group of American doctors has produced a report *(The Physicians' Task Force on Hunger in America)* showing, inter alia, that 20 million Americans go hungry, and that 3 million homeless, many of them mentally ill, roam the streets of big cities. Infant mortality is higher in the USA than in any other industrial country. Functionally illiterate adults number at least 60 million according to a Ford Foundation study. A Harvard University study puts the number somewhat higher at between 75 million and 78 million. One in three American families is affected by a serious crime each year. The homicide rate in the USA is the highest of any western country. American prisons house one and a half million inmates, the highest proportion of population of any country in the world (this usefully reduces the figures of male unemployment by 2%!).

And underlying all the above is the sober realisation that much of the apparent affluence in US society today is founded on debt. Personal debt apart, the amounts of national debt and external trade deficit increased grotesquely during and following the Reagan years. The first has been brought under control, but the latter is now seriously worrying many observers and, as already mentioned in connection with oil, threatens the stability of the world's financial systems.

As a corollary to the above, it is interesting to note that citizens of nearby Cuba (ostracised by the USA) enjoy higher literacy, lower infant mortality, longer average life-spans, and a far lower crime rate than do citizens of the immeasurably richer USA.

A reactionary regime, operating single-mindedly in the interests of the rich, can accelerate inequity in a capitalistic economy very quickly. The experience of the UK under the Thatcher regime of the 1980s is a case in point.

Interestingly, much of the change was achieved by, and is epitomised by, the British "privatisation" program, a transparent give-away to the rich. The sales, generally at firesale prices, of the privatised-to-be industries (which had previously belonged to the *whole* population!) were manifestly made only to those who had some capital to spare. The excess profits of the major privatised utilities, gouged out of domestic and industrial consumer alike, now alone amount to a staggering 10 billion Pounds per annum.

Privatisation also brought about the high-grading and destruction of British coal – by far and away Europe's largest single energy resource (yes, significantly larger than North Sea oil). It is worth explaining that, from a capitalist's viewpoint, the most profitable way of operating a mine is *not*, as one might have thought, by mining all the profitable ore! Rather, the "best" way is to mine out only the very richest ore (this is known as "high-grading") and leave the rest. In this way, the *rate* of profits is greatest, and the capitalist (like our whaler) can then take his profits and move on to repeat the process elsewhere. No matter that he leave behind collapsed and flooded workings which still contain much valuable ore but which may never again be accessible. In this way, as in so many others, the workings of everyday capitalism, notably its appetite for quick profit, discount our future to insignificance.

The proceeds of privatisation, along with huge temporary revenues from North Sea oil, massive cuts in government assistance to local council authorities, and the sell-off of council housing, enabled three successive Tory governments to dramatically lower taxes for the better off. While Britain's industrial base eroded away, these tax changes alone more than quadrupled the net income of wealthy parasites (such as Mister Thatcher) living idly off investments. Tory, incidentally, is an Irish word meaning robber.

Meanwhile, the rich could convert their ill-gotten money gains into tangible things such as real estate, land, gold, and profitable exploitive industry overseas (in which endeavour they have been immensely helped by the GATT trade agreement of December 1993).

Other results of "Thatcherism" included an underemployed and demoralised industrial workforce and a now chronic trade deficit, soon to worsen dramatically when North Sea oil production declines. In little over a decade the gap between rich and poor in British society widened out of all conscience and came to exceed that in Victorian times. The succeeding pseudo-socialist government of Anthony Blair has seemingly been content to preside over a continuation of this same trend. Despite overall affluence,

British society now exhibits much social decay and human misery: in the year 2000, one-third of the British population were living below the poverty line and one-sixth existed on the sub-poverty "income support" level.

> Wisdom and caution have got us where we are now.
>
> Margaret Thatcher on BBC 1's *Panorama*, 23 January 1988

It seems truly frightening to me how the public at large has come to accept debate in terms of the obscene jargon and narrow vision of economists – those brainwashed lackeys of the capitalist system and revered advisers of political nincompoops. Economists will always be found in large numbers to argue plausibly for "economically sound" policies regarding slavery, forests, whales, groundwater, coal, the "dash for gas", privatisation, and so on and so forth. For many years, leading textbooks on economics have had little or nothing to say about natural resources. If the latter were mentioned at all in passing, many of them were described, in the execrable jargon of economists, as "free goods", i.e. there for the taking.

The miserable pseudoscience of economics (the very name is a grim parody) in fact does little more than describe the process of terminal rape of Earth's natural resources – and thus the end of our future. Economists themselves could accurately be described as criminal pimps. The kindest treatment of them would be to certify them insane and lock them up. Similar sentiments have been more elegantly expressed by others:

> An economist is a person who knows the price of everything and the value of nothing.
>
> Oscar Wilde

> The wise man is informed in what is right, the inferior man in what will pay.
>
> Confucius

One is irresistibly reminded of Voltaire:

> If we believe in absurdities, we shall commit atrocities.

In the world of today, we can see the (atrocious) results of (absurd) capitalism most clearly in the manner of its exploitation of the Third World, to which it is now so profitably linked by the mechanism of money. Cash crops for export are commonly grown in sight of starving landless peasants. Groundnuts continued to be exported from Sahel countries in West Africa during the killing drought and famine in the 1970s. The export of meat from Ethiopia to Saudi Arabia continued during the Ethiopian famine of the 1980s. Africa, the continent with the poorest and least well-fed people, is a net exporter of protein food.

More generally, the servicing of debt incurred for dubious "development" (generally in the interests of overseas capitalists!) means that, despite some continuing "aid", the Third World is now being bled to the extent of about 30 billion dollars per year, which is the net sum being paid by them to the richer capitalist countries.

> In its everyday work UNICEF is brought up against a face of today's economic problems which is not seen in the corridors of financial power. It is the face of a young child.
>
> UNICEF Annual Report, 1988

Granted, capitalism is a very "efficient" vehicle for the short-term exploitation of Earth's natural resources to produce quick profits. But, as I have attempted to document, it is inherently impossible for a capitalist society to plan sensibly, either for justice or for a future.

The finiteness of natural resources means that there is only a finite (and now decreasing) "pie" to enjoy. The capitalist system ensures that a lucky few (not necessarily the worthiest) enjoy relatively enormous slices. That is all. Meanwhile, a great many others will have at best very little, and none at all in time of adversity.

> Anne found Jeremy sitting alone, numb with misery. She took his hand. "I'm sorry," she said. "It is God's will." He shook his head. "That's what they allus tell us. Crop failure. Empty bellies. But it's the poor He takes, never the rich."
>
> extract from *The Onedin Line: The Iron Ships* by Cyril Abraham

Given the crimes of rape of natural resources and of robbery of many in the final analysis, leading to increasing human despair and inequity, the resultant spread of squalor and crime, not to mention impending economic collapse, how does capitalism manage to maintain itself, let alone absolve itself?

The answer, as mentioned above, lies in the fact that capitalism can enlist very powerful forces in society. Moreover, although it may be daft it is not stupid. The response of capitalism to valid criticism, given as we have seen its completely immoral nature, and blind to the consequences of its actions, is really quite logical and predictable. Basically, its response follows four paths:

1. Hope that those without capital *won't notice* what is going on.
2. If they begin to notice, *con them* by all means available.
3. If it proves impossible to con them, *use force* against them.
4. Point out that *alternatives*, e.g. socialism, *don't work*.

The first response is now really more of historical interest. As Abraham Lincoln once remarked, you can't fool all of the people all of the time. This became increasingly apparent after they learned to read following the invention of printing. Also, there arose Renaissance concepts of natural justice, notably in the works of Rousseau. The American Declaration of Independence, although it conveniently and hypocritically overlooked both slavery and the appalling treatment of native peoples, had also contained a lot of annoying ideas about the rights of man. The French Revolution with its distasteful slogans of liberty, equality, etc., was rather nasty, too. For a time, however, European nouveaux-riches factory owners were grudgingly assimilated into the feudal aristocracy by marriage, and the vote remained restricted to right-thinking, responsible property owners. The spread of possibly harmful information and ideas among the working classes in 19th century Britain was braked by the imposition of a penal stamp duty on every single copy of a newspaper. Nevertheless, faced with the unwelcome gradual spread of ideals of democracy and the desirability of being seen to pay lip service to them, establishments, now mainly capitalistic, have reluctantly extended the franchise to all – but not in the UK, for example, to all adult women until well into the twentieth century, 1928 to be precise.

The capitalist system therefore, in those countries which pride themselves on being "democratic", has largely been brought to the second response, namely conning the unwashed into voting for it, and thus being able to continue the charade, for at least up to the next inevitable major depression and hopefully beyond. This conning utilises various approaches and techniques:

(a) Equating of democracy with "free enterprise" (for free enterprise read unfettered exploitation).

(b) Provision of (small) carrots as bribes for a broad middle class of voters while the poorest are ignored, even sneered at and called "lazy" or "naturally evil", and the rich laugh all the way to the bank.

(c) Debasement of values of society by their crude over-simplification into money terms alone (alas, one of Thatcherism's abiding legacies).

(d) Subversion of true education.

(e) Cheap appeals to religion, tradition, and "patriotism".

(f) Control of the media (much of it mind-rotting TV and gutter press) and associated advertising.

This conning is generally very successful indeed. Image advertising, for example, at present accounting for 6% of the American economy, is a crude but successful attempt to drug a population into accepting a capitalist state of affairs as a normal one. Most people seem to have swallowed the implicit argument that financial profitability is the criterion of what should be acceptable policy in our western industrialised societies – while all around them the evidence is mounting that this policy is suicidal!

The third response, brute force, is more commonly employed in Third World countries, where it is generally carried out by proxy using unsavoury dictators in collaboration with First-World secret government organisations such as the American CIA. First World countries themselves, however, are not without their own internal resources such as militarisation of the police, creation of a secret police (MI5 in the UK), persecution of dissidents (e.g., the bizarre former US "Committee of Un-American Activities"), etc.

Tragically, the rationale of the fourth response has considerable validity. There seems to be too much Adam in us for altruism to work successfully in groups much larger than the family. By and large, it is now a historical fact that capitalism has confronted and defeated socialism – which meant, at least in theory, no more than exploring ways to work together in our complex societies for the common good (not, one might have thought, inherently a bad idea).

Industrial capitalism is thus a ragbag of confidence tricks.

1. It is, and always has been, a confidence trick on the poor (in relative terms, but not necessarily, as I have acknowledged, for a while in absolute terms). Very significantly, these days the poor include people both inside and outside the rich and powerful capitalistic countries.
2. It is increasingly becoming a confidence trick on Earth`s very vulnerable environment and finite natural resources.
3. It is thus a confidence trick on the future of all of us, rich and poor, indeed of all life on this planet.

It is this last aspect that should perhaps cause even those who may consider themselves to be doing very nicely thankyou under the present scheme of things to pause and consider.

* * * * * * *

Of pigs and rabbits: A conundrum

This is a story about an island and, at last count, the 1,200 pigs and 4,800 rabbits who live there. They can see other islands in the far distance, but they have no means of travelling to them. Nor, apparently, has their own island ever been visited in the past. So they are effectively isolated. Their island, a pleasant place, grows grass and edible plants and fruit all the year round.

The pigs, however, eat too much and foul the ground excessively. They also dig up grass and valuable plants in order to build themselves luxury nests. Indeed, the more a pig acts in this manner to increase the *Gross Piggery Product* the more he is esteemed as a good worker and citizen by his fellow pigs. The pigs tend to bully the rabbits and to keep the sweetest and most nutritious plants for themselves, even taking them from deep inside rabbit territory, and leaving only the grass for the rabbits.

The rabbits, on the other hand, eat very little. In fact, many of them go hungry partly due to harassment by the pigs, each of whom in his or her lifetime consumes about forty times as much of the island's resources as does a rabbit. The rabbits nevertheless breed and reproduce themselves more quickly than do the pigs, and the grass around many of the rabbits' large burrows is so eaten down that it cannot support them adequately.

As a consequence of the burrowing and grazing by the rabbits and the rooting by the pigs, the fertile soil of the island is in many places being eroded and washed into the sea whenever it rains. The total population of pigs and rabbits is increasing. Soon, a point must be reached when, with less soil to grow food and with more animals, there may not be enough food for all of them. So the outlook is not very good.

Now it would be to the advantage of all the pigs and rabbits, and particularly of their children and of their yet unborn progeny, who will have to inhabit the island in the future, to restrain consumption. That is to say the pigs should desist from, or at least reduce, their greedy, wasteful, and dirty behaviour, and the rabbits should limit the size of their families.

But the curious fact is that it is not to the advantage of any individual pig or rabbit to heed this obvious advice. If a pig started consuming less, he would be judged a poor shiftless "hippie" pig by his fellows, and he could lose the strength to bully the rabbits and to pursue his wasteful but affluent life-style. Neither is it to the advantage of a rabbit to limit the size of his family. This is because the rabbits are very fond of their parents and look after them in their old age and when they are sick. They bring their parents food when they themselves may be hungry – few pigs do this quite so conscientiously. So, the more a pig consumes, the happier he or she feels. And the more children a rabbit has, the more secure he or she feels. Thus, neither the pigs nor the rabbits can personally see good reason to change their customary patterns of behaviour, even though these would seem to be contributing to their common downfall!

Some pigs have invented a supreme deity (in the form of a pig, naturally). Many of them believe, in spite of the evidence before their eyes of an increasingly overcrowded and eroding island home, that their *Pig-God Will Provide* for them whatever happens. If necessary, He will come for them in some unexplained manner. He may not, however, provide in this way for the rabbits who are said to be lazy and sinful, and either don't know of or don't believe in the Pig-God.

For their part, the rabbits, when not occupied in bare survival, may spend time admiring the infinite blue of the sea and the sky that surround them. They may listen to the sea breezes that sough among the branches of the few remaining trees of the island (the pigs have uprooted many of the trees, and some of the hungrier rabbits are gnawing at the remainder). They may recount old stories of the island when it had fewer pigs and grew more nice things to eat, and was a more leisurely and pleasant place altogether.

From time to time a few desperate rabbits attempt to resist the pigs, but the pigs are far too strong for them. The result is a bloody rabbit hunt that discourages other rabbits from doing the same. Failure by pigs to deal with uppity rabbits would be a grave breach of the pigs' sacred *Domino Theory.* To enforce this policy, the pigs now have terrible weapons of mass destruction, which they can employ without any risk to themselves. Any rabbit who attempts to acquire the same weapons becomes a legitimate target for extermination.

In addition to this, the animals seem to have an innate tendency to be pugnacious towards each other. They have organised themselves into several groups, identified by differently coloured pieces of straw stuck into their hairy ears or tied around their curly tails. Quite a few notable and aggressive leaders, such as Bennie, Dolphie, Galtie, Maggie, Ronnie, Saddie, and Slobbie, have each discovered on occasion a curious thing. By waving aloft a little tuft of the appropriately coloured straw, their own group of animals can be quickly rallied, excited, and made fighting mad in the induced belief that other animals are out to get them. This mass hysteria goes by the name of *Patriotism.*

This is a particularly useful phenomenon to exploit if a leader pig wishes to divert the attention of subject pigs from his or her own inadequacies, or decides on a campaign to steal other animals' property. For this reason, patriotism has long been sanctified by leader pigs and their entourages, for example in old dead-pig language as follows: *"Dulce et decorum est pro patria mori".*

Two of the bigger pig groups, the blues and the reds, were once so potentially well-armed and silly enough as to be able to kill each other to the last pig. In fact, so conditioned were they to the patriotic response, that the slightest signal, even a mistaken one, could easily have triggered them to do just this. However, the reds (who had even shown some bizarre signs of being sympathetic to the rabbits) backed down and conflict was avoided.

Thus the blue pigs and their sycophantic followers can now get down to the proper business of keeping the rabbits in their place, taking from the rabbits what little they might have, and indeed ransacking the whole island.

Now you might well agree that none of the above behaviour and attitudes forms a practical or desirable basis for dealing with the very real long-term problems that now face the island and its inhabitants. Furthermore, it is just possible in your travels that you may have come across a similar island, also facing problems. Perhaps your own experiences might enable you to embroider some details on to this brief account.

The prospects for the animals on their beleaguered island seem bleak, and this leads to a conundrum: What would you do in this situation if you were (a) a pig, or (b) a rabbit?

I should mention that both the pigs and the rabbits are not bad fellows at heart when you get to know them. Although many are genuinely unaware of the extent of their predicament, they are all quite clever and can comprehend everything you say to them. Just a few of them, who have read island history books and know the island and its resources well and keep an open mind and an open heart, fully understand the conundrum. They are still searching for practical answers and would really appreciate your help.

* * * * * * *

What might have been

> One thing is certain: without learning from the past, you cannot hope to understand the present and without understanding the present you cannot shape a worthwhile future.
>
> Peter Berresford Ellis

> The most important truths are likely to be those which society least wants to hear.
>
> W.H.Auden & L.Kronenberger

> Take advice from him who makes you cry, and not from him who makes you laugh.
>
> Arab proverb

I came to spend many years of observing, reading, teaching, liaising and thinking on these interlinked matters many of which were, I have to say, once very novel to me. During this period I became very much aware that a geologist's insight into current affairs, although vitally important, was certainly not the only avenue to understanding. I found that there was a surprising convergence of informed opinion coming from some other natural scientists, from philosophers, humanists and environmentalists, even from a few informed radical economists, and indeed from many individuals in all walks of life. During my learning period, this was a very heartening discovery. If one kept ones eyes, ears, and heart open, one could learn a great deal. The whole would be typical of what Toynbee once called the reaction of a "creative minority" at the time of a civilisation in crisis.

When one reflects, it all comes down to a question of true education.

> If you plan for one year, plant rice. If you plan for ten, plant trees.
> If you plan for one hundred years, educate mankind.
>
> Kuan-Tzu

The only way for a democracy to follow sane policies with any prospect of hope for a future is indeed for people to be educated and informed. Otherwise, they will be the prey of cheap and ignorant liars such as capitalists, economists, press and TV barons, the advertising industry, and our contemporary brand of mentally sick politicians, all paying for known techniques of mind persuasion and "spin". The range of information necessary to combat this incessant brain-washing is surprisingly wide, but could be briefly summarised in the following prospectus:

(a) Earth history.

(b) Our physical environment on planet Earth.

(c) Life: the fossil record.

(d) Life today: ecology, Gaia.

(e) *Homo sapiens* in prehistory.

(f) History in resource terms: the rise and fall of civilisations.

(g) Humankind's intellectual and spiritual achievements, philosophy, comparative religion, especially Buddhism, literature, biography.

(h) Man's technological achievements, science, the industrial revolution.

(i) The population explosion, urbanisation, the family, birth control, responsible parenthood.

(j) Natural resource depletion, pollution, environmental destruction.

(k) Current affairs, social ethics, a conservationist ethic.

(l) Individual purpose in life.

The above should form the basis of education in all our schools. All teachers should be instructed in this programme for certification (or recertification!). It does not have to be taught at the expense of the three R's etc. Children of all ages and ability levels can appreciate it. It leads to the tapping of our innate conscience (capitalist society incessantly strives to muzzle this) and to true ethics along rational lines. At first glance, it may sound far too tough – a whole "liberal education" at school level! But it is a logical sequence forming a reinforcing framework of knowledge and understanding.

The theme of Rousseau's *Social Contract*, the essential compromise between man's desire for individual freedom on the one hand, and his need for laws on the other hand, i.e. the balance between "rights" and "duties" in society, should be the basis of continuing study and debate. The parameters of this debate may have to include, in our unique and rapidly developing crisis, a new asceticism and a consideration of what to attempt to preserve as our per capita stock of natural resources and our material affluence inevitably decline.

> The essence of education is that it be religious.
>
> Alfred North Whitehead

One would learn, as the central part of one's existence, to humbly thank God for the incredible gift of life on this lovely planet. As memorably put by Adlai Stevenson in 1965:

> We travel together, passengers in a little spaceship, dependent on its vulnerable reserves of air and soil; all committed for our safety to its security and peace; preserved from annihilation only by the care, the work and, I will say, the love we give our fragile craft.

Out of all this there would be both perceived and accepted the need of a paradigm change, beginning in the individual minds and hearts of men and women. As Albert Camus once wrote:

> Great ideas come into the world as gently as doves. Perhaps, then, if we listen attentively, we shall hear, amid the uproar of empires and nations, a faint flutter of wings, the gentle stirrings of life and hope. Some will say that this hope lies in a nation; others in a man. I believe, rather, that it is awakened, revived, nourished by millions of solitary individuals whose deeds and works every day negate frontiers and the crudest implications of history.

The paradigm shift that Man must now collectively make is to view Earth not as something to exploit for his own selfish purposes of the present, but as the host of something of fragile beauty which has become his unique responsibility to preserve. Coupled with faith in man, an appreciation and love of Gaia must be the basis of ethics. Man matters more than dogma or profits, and Gaia matters more than man. We must all humbly approach this "religious" truth.

Everything else follows from the above. Paradoxically, this apparent self-sacrifice by Man seems to be the only way to ensure the sustainability of Man on Earth. What is likely to prove man's "last frontier" is no longer the oceans, or prairies, or space, but the extent of his comprehension, both rational and psychic, of Gaia.

> There is a growing volume of evidence to show that we are moving into a new phase of history when we shall have to develop a new economics linked to a new environmentalism.
>
> Harford Thomas

> So the great quest had to be started all over again; the human caravan must needs set forth once more, this time along a new road, and heading for a different goal.
>
> Paul Hazard

> The fashion in which we think changes like the fashion of our clothes, and it is difficult, if not impossible, for most people to think otherwise than in the fashion of their own period.
>
> George Bernard Shaw

> We shall continue to have a worsening ecologic crisis until we reject the Christian axiom that nature has no reason for existence save to serve man. Since the roots of our trouble are so largely religious, the remedy must also be essentially religious, whether we call it that or not. We must rethink and refeel our nature and destiny.
>
> Lynn White

The way will certainly not be easy, well-defined, or free of controversy. One will never arrive at a utopia. There will always be debate and dissent, and some inevitable inequity, injustice, and imperfections. But at least there might be some prospect of a future.

There is a lovely little outport, one of a great many, in Newfoundland called Happy Adventure. We should strive to ensure that life on Earth is a "happy adventure" for all. And, adding the dimension of time (never far from a geologist's thinking), we should strive to ensure a similar prospect for the generations to come.

I seem to have fallen into the trap of speaking in the present and future tenses, albeit tempered by the conditional, of what could have been possible. But I fear it may be too late.

* * * * * * *

What now looks probable

It will be apparent that I once worked as a "scientist", attempting to comprehend a range of facts relevant to an appreciation of our human situation on planet Earth, i.e., *what is now*. My conclusion was that there were rational grounds for *concern*.

Then I attempted to think more deeply as a "humanist", concerned about options for the future, i.e., *what could be*. My conclusion was that there were grounds for *hope*. What are we here for? To maximise the GNP, to provide wealth for a relative few, to pollute, to destroy, to exterminate, to create a living hell and potential extinction for our children? A growing movement of people drawn from all walks of society, and with a fascinating literature in many disciplines, has said NO to all this and has offered alternatives.

Now, however, I must speak as a "realist", taking a cold look at the evidence presented by contemporary history and current affairs, i.e., *what is likely*. The results are *disturbing*. I can only echo Lewis Mumford who once stated that he was "an optimist about the possibilities and a pessimist about the probabilities for mankind."

It is my sad conclusion that there is now enough evidence to answer Heilbroners's delicately expressed query, quoted above. The answer is a (qualified) NO, there is little hope for man – at least, for industrial "civilised" man. For the energy, environment, population, and social time-bombs continue to tick away, and it seems alas that it may now be too late to defuse them.

Time is indeed slipping away from us. Now that the high-water mark of material affluence for mankind on Earth is passing, selfishness, greed, ignorance, fear and desperation are effectively strangling hope for a sustainable future.

A rapidly growing and increasingly hopeless urbanised proletariat is becoming debased and ineducable. Incredibly crass and corrupt monetarist regimes have assumed power in many countries, with yapping puppets as their mouthpieces. These politicians work for the short-term interests of the rich and powerful and receive huge bribes for doing so, while everywhere the poorer in society suffer increasing hardship.

It seems that the world is now on the point of slowly but surely entering an uncomfortable post-industrial Dark Age just as Britain was to enter a post-Roman Dark Age in the early 5th century. Not many living in Britain in A.D.410 might have thought that the letter of Honorius was final. Nor might they have foreseen the horrors of the Dark Age that was to descend on them so inexorably over the following century, despite the evidence before their eyes of its commencing.

Similarly, there are many unpalatable things which we see happening in the world today. But we still tend to regard them as abnormal events, which will somehow come right in time. These include unemployment, inflation, crime, vandalism, terrorism, Third-World crises, environmental catastrophes, starvation, disease, ethnic cleansing, and vicious predatory wars. It would be nice if all this were to diminish and just go away, but what if it were to grow and coalesce, and come to encompass even more widespread poverty, social anarchy, and environmental collapse – become normal in fact? – what then?

Man, particularly "civilised" industrial man, may thus prove to have been a bizarre, unique, and extremely short-lived evolutionary experiment, predicated on a ludicrous over-specialization in brain-power and on a fleeting exploitation of Earth's fossil fuels.

Although *Homo sapiens* is undoubtedly brainy, it is interesting to note that the successful social animal, the ant, has an even larger brain in proportion to its size. Perhaps we are not brainy enough! But then, who wants to live the life-style of an ant? What does it all matter, anyway? The stars will keep on turning.

TOMORROW'S PAST

We are tomorrow's past,
We cast a shadow,
write a page in history's growing tome.
In time to come
our own – this present age –
like ancient Greece and Rome shall disappear.
No throne can long endure,
each has its day – and all must someday end.
We are tomorrow's past,
unless, through folly, our today
becomes for all mankind
the last.

John Andrew Storey

The irony, it seems to me, is that humankind has never been better equipped in terms of knowledge and materiel to cope with coming crisis than it is at the present day. What are lacking are the ingredients of true education, understanding, wisdom, an appreciation of true values and a sense of purpose. We are thus incapable of making the essential "ethical" response to what may appear to us to be merely "technical" problems. And, critically, our apathy renders time our enemy.

We are denying our innate potentials for rational thought, spirituality, and compassion. We are denying and perverting the approaches and teachings of Buddha, Jesus, Gandhi, and others among our great spiritual leaders.

> The Earth has enough for every man's need, but not for every man's greed.
>
> Mahatma Gandhi

But the psychic roots of humankind will endure and perhaps a higher proportion of a drastically reduced world population will come to live in touch with them.

Out of chaos, poverty, and despair could a new "Age of Saints" somewhere arise? The one I once studied and came to love possessed very little in the way of material resources. Will a new generation of Saints properly worship Gaia? Will they ever remember us at all? If they do, what tiny fraction of our literature and achievements will they consider to be of value and worth the keeping and patient copying? – certainly not the insane and obscene gibberish of contemporary economists and politicians! Will a race-memory survive of Arthur, that noble but all too human man, once king and king to be, who strove for the ideal of the common good?

As I have said, it is impossible for me to express in prose the depth of my gratitude for the miraculous gift of life on this lovely planet. I have enjoyed it so much. My dearest wish still, my dying wish, would be that my children and their children and children everywhere will in years to come be able to feel the same.

My sadness, a most profound sadness, is the suspicion that they may not. As a participant in the unheeding present, I now view my wealth and many of my possessions with distaste. I am left with a deep sense of sadness and guilt and foreboding for the future, coupled with uncertainty.

> I guarded the feeling of hope in my breast;
> My eyes glowed with the joy of life,
> Whose magic held me fast,
> Whenever I listened to its flattering voice.
> Its echo now is lost in life's storm.
> Be still my heart; think not on it,
> For this now is truth; the other, madness.
>
> Translated from *Sei still mein Herz* by Carl B.V.Schweitzer

> Great truths do not take hold of the hearts of the masses. And now, as all the world is in error, how shall I, though I know the true path,

> how shall I guide? If I know that I cannot succeed and yet try to force success, this would be another source of error. Better then to desist and strive no more. But if I do not strive, who will?
>
> Chuang-tse

So what can one do? In answer to this question, which I have only come to perceive and pose near the end of my own tiny Odyssey on Earth, I can only repeat the vow I once made on Bardsey – namely, to work for the remainder of my days so as to make a humble contribution to a (quixotic?) ideal – that a proper understanding and love of Gaia might come to inspire some who may survive the coming Dark Age, just as the love of Christ once unforgettably inspired those who once survived a terrible Dark Age on the Celtic fringe of Europe.

EPILOGUE

Did Chalwyn go a little mad (as some claimed)? Perhaps I should leave it to those who may read this book to judge for themselves. But over the years I think I can claim to have known Chalwyn better than any of his colleagues. And I would say that, although unconventional in his interests and ideas, Chalwyn remained entirely logical to the end. I recall him once saying that his desire was merely to "extract the spiritual from a mis-spent life". In many ways I eventually came to understand and agree with him. I would go so far as to say that we became as one.

Nigel Baird